The Size of Your Dreams

A Novel that Transforms Lives

by Dave and Chana Mason

D1452907

Cover design by the Amazing Juan Hernaz
JuanHernaz.com

To our lion-hearted son, Aryeh Lev,
who's joined us every step of
the way on this crazy adventure.

Chapter One

The New Math

"*What is my goal in taking this class?*" Jarod Miller stared at the sheet in his hands, eyebrows shooting up. "What kind of math test is this?"

"I never called it a math test," Mr. Griffin said.

Trigonometry had been a disaster ever since Mr. Higgs suffered a stroke in late September. They'd transferred as many students as possible into Mrs. Northrup's class but had to stop when they hit the 30 student limit. During the weeks since, the school shuffled in a stream of substitutes, and most of the remaining students dropped out, leaving just four of us, all seniors. None of us knew where they dug up Mr. Griffin.

Despite there only being four of us left, Jarod moved right past me to the back of the room, because Jarod always sat in the back. His hair still had that just-got-out-of-bed rustle, though it was already fifth period. Stout and muscular, ahe could have been an athlete but gave up sports years ago when he gave up everything else school related. His main workouts now came behind a lawnmower or snow blower.

"Oh no!" Christy Mendez walked in and took a paper. "You're handing out a test? That's so unfair."

"Is there a problem, Christy?"

"You know my name?"

"Yes, I know all of your names." Mr. Griffin's piercing blue eyes caught each of ours. I couldn't help but look away. "Now the problem?"

"You haven't taught us anything yet."

"Agreed. This is to make sure we change that."

Christy mouthed to Jarod, "you've got to be kidding me" and eased into the seat next to his. She eyed Mr. Griffin as she pulled her coffee-colored hair into a ponytail. Besides being captain of the girls' swim team, Christy studied harder than almost anyone. She was sizing up this new guy—she needed trig to get into college.

Darnell Jones lugged himself in, sweaty and winded, just as the bell rang. Jarod liked to joke that Darnell and Billy Jenks were playing a chess match to see who would graduate the fattest, with Billy playing the white pieces, and Darnell, one of only a handful of African Americans in school, playing the black. Darnell squeezed his oversized frame into the desk next to mine and tipped a quick nod in my direction.

"Whatever you call this paper, isn't the answer obvious?" Jarod asked.

"Is it, Jarod? Perhaps I've underestimated you. Today is, after all, my first day teaching. How about you go ahead and fill it out, and we'll see how obvious it is. Fifteen minutes should be enough."

Mr. Griffin sat atop one of the student desks, reading off some note cards and mumbling to himself. He was a surprisingly tall figure. Trimly cropped black hair topped his lean face. He wore a raven-black dress shirt and khakis that fell smoothly over his loafers. His legs pumped back and forth, showing off purple polka-dotted socks.

"Not looking good," Jarod whispered to Christy. "Even I can read without moving my lips."

It only took me a few seconds to answer the question. When I finished, everyone except Darnell had stopped writing. A moment later, his pencil hit the table as well.

Mr. Griffin was so immersed in his notecards, he didn't even notice we were all done. "Uh, Mr. Griffin?" I said.

He looked up from his cards. "Yes, Kelvin? Do you need me to clarify the assignment?"

"No. It's just…. We're all done."

"All of you?" He scanned the room. "Already?"

"Well, yeah," Darnell said. "The question was kind of easy."

"Was it? Personally, I consider it to be quite difficult. But pass back your papers. Let's see how you've all done."

Jarod grabbed Christy's and stretched forward to pass theirs up to me. With three rows of empty chairs between us, I still had to get up to take them. I grabbed Darnell's on my way back and handed all four to Mr. Griffin.

"Darnell," Mr. Griffin said, "you wrote that your goal this year is to learn trigonometry. Why is that important to you?

Darnell shrugged. "It's important stuff to know."

"Is it? Can you give me one example of how you anticipate using trigonometry later in your life?"

Darnell wiped his forehead with the back of his sleeve. "Uh..."

"Your homework, Darnell, will be to ask your parents what math skills they still use and try to ascertain in what grade they learned them. The answer might surprise you."

Mr. Griffin turned to my test. "Kelvin, your goal is to learn how to think better. Are you saying that trigonometry is like a game to test your mind?"

"Yeah, sort of," I said. "It helps you think analytically."

"And do you believe trigonometry is the most effective tool available for teaching analytical thinking? Do you find that math pushes you to your intellectual limits, Kelvin?"

"Not really. I usually get A's without trying too hard."

Jarod scoffed behind me.

"Oh leave him alone, Jarod," Christy said. "It may not come as easy for me as for Kelvin, but I'm also here to get an A."

"Indeed," Mr. Griffin said, "getting an A was what you listed as your goal. Why is that important to you?"

"I need to get a scholarship for college."

"Come on, Christy," Jarod said, "if you get a scholarship it's going to be for your swimming. You're better off working on your breaststroke."

"Grades can play a role too, especially at the better schools. Besides, now that coach is gone, I doubt my times will improve any."

"And you, Jarod?" Mr. Griffin said. "Care to share with the class what you wrote?"

"I'm here for one reason and one reason only. To graduate. I need one more math credit before they'll let me out of this place."

"So your goal in this class is just to get through it?"

"Pretty much."

"Well, it's nice to know that each of you has such low expectations," Mr. Griffin said. "That certainly takes pressure off me. I expect we can achieve most of that quite easily."

Low expectations? Collectively we'd said that we wanted to learn the subject matter, strengthen our thinking abilities, get good grades, and fulfill our educational requirements. What else were we in school for? I raised my hand, but didn't wait to be called on before saying, "What about you, Mr. Griffin? You seem unimpressed with our goals for the class. What are yours?"

"I'm glad you asked, Kelvin." Mr. Griffin picked up a notecard from his desk and read:

> *My goal for my trigonometry class is to instill in my students a glimpse of the greatness they have within them and to provide tools to help them succeed in life: emotionally, physically, spiritually, and financially.*

"What the…" Jarod mumbled so quietly I couldn't hear the rest of his words.

Darnell said, "Isn't one of your goals to teach us math?"

"Oh right, I should probably add that." Mr. Griffin grabbed a pen and wrote below his other goals. He then read out:

> *And get all students to master the State approved curriculum for this class.*

At this point, we were speechless. Mr. Griffin passed back our papers. "You all filled these out quite quickly the first time. Take the rest of today's class and tonight to rethink your answers. That will be your homework. Darnell, remember you have an additional assignment, to check with your parents regarding the math they use in their lives."

* * *

My 12-year-old sister Megan dragged her feet across the floor as she came in for dinner. Random strings of dirty-blond hair fluttered out of her braid.

"Everything okay at school, sweetie?" Mom placed her hand on Megan's shoulder, but she slunk out of reach.

"It was fine." My sister slid into her chair.

Mom served us chicken, peas, and mashed potatoes. I got a double serving of the mash, my favorite.

She turned to me. "How about you? How was school?"

"Fine. We finally got a new math teacher," I said, before shoving a forkful of chicken into my mouth.

"So perhaps you'll be able to learn trig this year, after all."

"Maybe," I mumbled.

"You don't like him?"

"I dunno. He's kinda weird. I still wish I was in calculus this year."

"This again?" My father asked, glancing up from his research study. It was his fault that I was in trig this year rather than in calculus. When the rest of the advanced math class had gone on to trig last year, he insisted that I take Stats instead. "Statistics are key to understanding data, and data is everywhere. A recent study by the New England Journal of Medicine showed that 5 out of 4 doctors don't understand basic statistics, and they're supposed to be scientists." Dad grinned at his own joke. "You'll thank me for it one day."

I wasn't feeling too thankful at the moment, but I kept my mouth shut. As a neurobiology professor, Dad used statistics all the time in his work, so I couldn't deny their value. But had I taken trig with the rest of my class I could be in calculus now with a normal teacher, rather than stuck with Mr. Griffin.

"How is the new teacher weird?" Mom always broke in with a change of subject when Dad and I got to arguing.

"I dunno, Mom, just weird, okay?"

My mom, as usual, let the subject drop. Megan piped in, "Weird like you, maybe?"

"Shut up, Megan."

I was more curious about this new teacher than I let on to my family. That night I quickly worked through my homework for my other subjects, then dived into math. I didn't spend any time thinking over Mr. Griffin's idiotic question, though. No math teacher showed up the first day of class and forgot he was supposed to be teaching us math. There was something strange about this guy, and I intended to find out what it was.

The problem was, Griffin wasn't such an uncommon name, and teachers weren't known to leave deep digital footprints. Still, one of my counselors at Hacker Camp used to say that with enough skill and perseverance, you could find information on anyone. I'd been programming since before I could ride a bike, so no issue with my computer skills. And my parents almost never checked on me after I went to bed, so as long as I didn't make too much noise, I could stay up all night if I had to.

I had two computers in my room (one a Mac, the other an old PC that I'd converted to Linux) and a total of four monitors. I powered them all on and prepared to dig in. The school website didn't have him listed, but I found a notice on the Superintendent's site mentioning he'd been hired to take over Mr. Higgs' trigonometry class for the rest of the year. That was odd; I assumed he'd take over all of Mr. Higgs' classes, but it was just ours. More importantly, I got the piece of information I'd been looking for: his first name. It is far easier to search for people with unusual names—you don't get so many false positives. So when I saw that his first name was Mark, I knew I was out of luck.

I pulled up a digital notepad and typed in all I knew. It wasn't much. His name was far too common to be of much use. He was only part-time at the school and had just started teaching there, so he likely hadn't even updated his LinkedIn profile with the school name yet—if he even had one. He was teaching math, but this bizarre first day made me doubt he'd ever taught before, much less have a teaching degree. The one thing I felt confident about was location. He wouldn't commute more than 30 miles to get to some part-time teaching job. There were no more than ten towns within that radius, so I'd start by searching his name followed by each of the town names until I found all of the Mark Griffins living in this part of the state.

I dragged my notepad to my secondary monitor and opened a browser on my main one. Though I knew it was pointless, I started off with just the most general search, typing only his name into the search bar.

And there he was. Just like that. First page, first result. I knew it was the same Mark Griffin because Google posted a picture of him in the right column, along with a link to his Wikipedia page. His Wikipedia page? He must be the first teacher in the history of our school, perhaps the first teacher of *any* school, with his own Wikipedia page.

Ding. It was Darnell on chat.

"Hey," he wrote. "Some first day of math, eh?"

"No kidding. How are you doing?"

"Still reeling from last night's game. I can't believe I didn't start Gurley."

I didn't share Darnell's love of football, but I nonetheless let him talk me into joining his fantasy league. I hadn't even checked the scores yet this week. "He had a good game?"

"198 yards and two touchdowns. Man, I wish I could run like that."

As the fattest, slowest kid I knew, Darnell could barely run down the hall, much less a football field. I ignored his comment, and typed, "BTW, Mr. Griffin has his own Wikipedia page."

"No way!!!!" Darnell wrote. "Send me the link."

I copied and pasted it over, then dived into the article. Turns out he studied machine learning and artificial intelligence at MIT, the same school I was hoping to attend. Then he went to work building high-volume stock market trading machines for some investment bank I'd never heard of. He left after three years and began a data mining startup, apparently self-funding it with earnings from his banking job. Last year he sold the company to Oracle.

"It says he sold his business for some undisclosed amount," Darnell wrote. "How much do you think that is?"

"No clue, but enough that he doesn't need the salary from a part-time teaching job."

"So what's he doing here?"

"Your guess is as good as mine." I sent the link to Christy and Jarod, who despite not having much to do with me in school were still my Facebook "friends." I pulled out the "test" from math class where I'd written that my goal was "To learn how to think better." It was such an obvious answer at the time, though Mr. Griffin had been unimpressed.

As much as he seemed like a kook in class, everything I'd just learned about Mr. Griffin made me wonder, what should my answer be?

Chapter Two

The Power of Incentives

"You're staring." Wally elbowed my arm.

I'd just finished my sandwich, and my eyes had wandered over to Christy's table. Where Monica Gray sat. My attention quickly found its way back to the apple in my hand. "No, I'm not."

"Kelvin, who do you think you're kidding? She doesn't even know your name."

"Sure she does. We had lab together last year."

"You had lab with who?"

"Monica."

"You mean the girl you *weren't* staring at?" Wally slapped his leg and chortled. He was the only kid in school who could program as well as I could, and he always looked for opportunities to outsmart me.

"Ha ha," I said, wanting to bring the conversation to an end as quickly as I could. I also enjoyed one-upping Wally, and of the two of us, I had the sharper wit. But Monica was turning in our direction now. It was bad enough that my face was breaking out worse than ever today. Being seen hanging out with Wally Hoster, whose hair was so greasy he could shape it without gel, was enough to earn social exile. Mind, I was already sitting next to him, but that was just because it beat sitting alone. Barely.

"There's no point anyway." Bits of egg salad sprayed out of Wally's mouth as he spoke. "It's not like she's gonna follow you to MIT."

* * *

When Jarod sat down in the second to last row, I knew my message about Mr. Griffin had piqued his interest. Christy sat in the desk in front of him. Even Darnell made a special effort to get to class before the bell, which left him sweatier than usual.

Mr. Griffin sat at his desk reading his notecards. When the bell rang, he put them down and stepped to the front of the class.

"Darnell, tell us about your homework."

Darnell was still huffing when he said, "I asked my folks what math they used, and the only things they could think of were addition, subtraction, multiplication, division, and fractions, all of which they learned by the 5th grade."

"Interesting. What do—?"

"Wait," he put up his hand, "there's more. Then I called my uncle. He couldn't think of any time he used advanced math either, but my aunt said she uses it in her job every day."

"And what does she do?"

Darnell grinned. "She's a high school math teacher."

Mr. Griffin raised an eyebrow. "So what do you take away from all of this?"

Darnell huffed out one final breath. "I'm mostly confused. Usually, teachers try to get us more interested in their subjects, you seem to want us to be less interested."

"Not at all. I just want you to understand the limitations of the curriculum alone."

I broke in. "The school must consider the curriculum valuable. Otherwise, they wouldn't require it."

Jarod scoffed. "The curriculum is like a hundred years old. It's not like they update it for the times."

"Don't discard something just because it's old," Mr. Griffin said. "The techniques I use every day are more than a hundred years old, and I've still never found anything more potent. Nonetheless, I agree that mastering the material in your classes is no longer the ticket to success or even employment that it once was."

"Does this mean you're not going to teach us math?" Christy asked.

"I've been hired to be your math teacher. Despite what others may think of my techniques, I always live up to my obligations. Speaking of which, I'd like hear how all of you expanded on yesterday's assignment."

I bit my lip. Despite my late-night efforts, I hadn't added a word to my page. Judging from the silence in the room, I wasn't alone.

After a painfully long delay, Mr. Griffin said, "I see." He slowly paced down one of the empty aisles of the classroom, rolling a pen between his fingers.

When he reached the last desk, he punctured the air with the pen. "I've got it. I know why you're all struggling to put effort into yesterday's assignment."

"Because it's ridiculously easy?" Jarod suggested.

"No, because it's ridiculously hard. It was unfair of me to give you such a task on day one. Indeed, I see now that I violated one of my core principles."

"Which is what?" Christy asked.

"To always start with vision. I tried, but I defined my question far too narrowly to get you there."

Jarod stretched his hands out before him and moved them around an imaginary orb. Speaking with the thick accent of a fortune teller at a fair, he said, "I envision passing trigonometry so I can get out of this school."

"Precisely," Mr. Griffin said. "All you want to do is leave school because you have no compelling vision of what you want to get from school."

Jarod's hands dropped. He stared back, silent.

"Does that mean," Darnell said, "that you want to change the question from what we hope to get out of trigonometry to what we hope to get out of school?"

"No, no, no Darnell, it's still too narrow. How can you know what you want to get out of school without first knowing what you want out of life?"

Mr. Griffin was practically bouncing, but I couldn't share his enthusiasm.

"I totally know what I want to do," Christy said. "I want to become a physical therapist."

"Very good. If you know what you want to do for a living, you're already ahead of most. But I don't just want a vision for your job—I want a vision for your *life*. That includes a vision for your home, family, and community. For how you spend time *outside* of work, not just *in* it."

"Ugh." Christy rolled her eyes and crossed her arms. "Why is it that whenever a woman brings up career, the automatic response is that she has to think about family?"

"As a woman, it's more likely that you've at least given it some thought," Mr. Griffin said. "Most men never give family a moment's consideration until it's too late."

"How's it ever too late?" Darnell asked.

Mr. Griffin sighed. "I can't tell you how many of my peers spent a fortune in tuition and years of their lives pursuing careers that only lasted two or three years because they suddenly had a family and found their jobs incompatible."

Christy's arms unclenched.

I thought about my own plans. I always dreamed of working for some hard-core start-up. The programmers I met who'd gone down that path didn't just work 80 hour weeks, they bragged about it. Somehow, I'd never given any thought to having a family at the same time. Did I really want to have kids but never see them?

"So how am I supposed to get a vision for my life?" Darnell asked.

"Here's a very simple exercise. Close your eyes. Go on Jarod—I'm not going to throw anything at you. Good. Take three slow, deep breaths."

My body sank deeper into my seat.

Mr. Griffin's voice grew softer. "Now, imagine yourself twenty years in the future. You're happy. Life has been good to you. You feel tremendously grateful that everything has fallen into place. Look around you."

"All I see is an empty math class," Jarod said.

"Eyes closed, Jarod. I want you to visualize your future. What does your life look like?" He paused. I immediately saw an image of working at a startup. "Are you married?"

My initial thought was yes, but I couldn't envision that.

"Do you have children? Where do you live? What do you do? How do you contribute to others?" The questions came faster now, and while visions flashed across my mind, I couldn't hold all of them. "Open your eyes, and write down what you saw."

Mr. Griffin paced back to his chair, sat down, and propped his heels up on his desk. He pulled a tattered book out of his briefcase. I tilted my head to get a look at the cover. *Think and Grow Rich*. He opened to a dog-eared page in the middle of the tome and said, "You have until the end of class."

The first thing I wrote about was my career. That part was easy. I knew I wanted to create world-changing technologies. Like Tesla. Not Tesla now, with its billions of dollars in income, but like Tesla when they first started out.

As to where I'd live, that was also easy. There were really only a few options for that type of work. Silicon Valley, Seattle, Austin. I'd put down Austin for now; it was more up and coming.

That's when I got stuck. *Marriage? Children? Community?*

I put down my pen and looked around the class. Mr. Griffin was still absorbed in his book. Christy was bent over her paper, had already written a full page, and was still going strong. Jarod was leaning back, playing with his Leatherman. His sheet of paper was glaringly white for its blankness. Darnell had his pen close to the top of his page and was staring up at the ceiling, looking for answers.

I returned to my own paper. *Why was this so difficult?* Not a day went by when I didn't think about having more friends, and hardly an hour when I didn't think about having a girlfriend. That's really all Mr. Griffin had asked us to do, to think about what we wanted in life. So why was I all of a sudden drawing a blank?

* * *

The next morning, I dragged myself out of bed and moved through the house like a soggy mop. My mother eyed me all through breakfast, but she knew better than to ask me questions that early in the day. Megan read her Kindle while she ate, paying me no mind.

I had flitted in and out of sleep the night before, haunted by a recurring dream about living at some high-tech start-up with a blow-up mattress, a nightlight, and a teddy bear stored under my cubicle desk. I spent dark, cold nights there alone with only microwave pizza to keep me company. Everything felt so incredibly normal, but I woke up in sweats each time the microwave beeped that the pizza was ready. Was this my future?

I had a hard time keeping my eyes, or even my mind, open during the first few hours of the day. By the time fifth period came around, I was ready to crawl into the janitor's closet and use *his* mop as a pillow. Beside my exhaustion was the uneasy feeling that I'd have to revisit my nightmare during Mr. Griffin's class. Plus, I hadn't completed his assignment. I never did that.

"Okay, what have you all got?" Mr. Griffin said as soon as we were all seated. "Jarod?"

"This assignment was lame." The thick rubber soles of his work-boots drummed against the leg of his desk. "What kinda math class is this anyhow?"

"Lame," Mr. Griffin said. "I see...So, you don't have any plans for your future?"

"Just the same crap as everyone else. College, job, wife, kids, house, retire, die. What's there to write?"

Mr. Griffin looked at the rest of us. "You all have something like this?"

"More or less...," Christy's shoulders rose to meet her ears. She'd written a hundred times more than Jarod and ten times more than I had. Did everything she jotted down really get summed up by Jarod in just a few words? Mine didn't even get that far.

"I thought our visions were pretty lame," Jarod said, "but you seem mighty impressed."

Mr. Griffin indeed was practically bouncing at the front of the class. "Impressed? Hardly. I'm excited by their very lameness."

"You like lame?" Christy asked.

"Absolutely. It tells me that, like most people, you've never given much thought to your life goals."

"And that's good?" I asked.

"For me it is. I don't teach for the benefits, and certainly not for the salary.

I'm here because I want to create lasting change. Frankly, I'm new at this. I had no idea how easy or hard this would be. But now that I see you've all set the bar so low, I do not doubt that I can completely revolutionize your lives this year."

Mr. Griffin may have been grinning from ear to ear, but we couldn't share his enthusiasm. Was he really telling us all that we were pathetic and mindless? And this was *good* news because he was going to somehow fix us?

"You still didn't answer my question." Jarod kicked the legs of his desk. "What does this have to do with math?"

"If I do my job well, you'll find within yourself the ability to go as far as you want with your mathematics. Nonetheless, my core goal as your teacher is not confined to math."

Christy leaned forward in her chair. "So what is your goal?"

"My goal is to activate your minds, to give you the tools to succeed no matter what direction you take."

If I hadn't read the article on him the other night, I wouldn't have given his words much credence. But this guy was no stranger to success.

Jarod, however, was more interested in what it would cost him. "You're going to do this by the end of the year, *on top* of teaching us math? Just how much homework do you plan on giving us?"

"Five minutes a day."

"Five minutes? That's it?"

"That's all it will take to implement my basic techniques. Beyond that, I expect you'll each want to push yourselves to do more. But those will be *your* steps toward *your* goals, not mine."

"What are these techniques?" I asked. "You said they were a hundred years old?"

"If you dig deep enough, you'll find variations in use even thousands of years ago. But the first time I know they were written down was in 1937."

"Who wrote them?"

"Napoleon Hill."

Jarod scoffed. "That French dude?"

Christy slapped his shoulder. "That was Napoleon Bonaparte. We just learned about him in European history last year. Where were you?"

"Who's Napoleon Hill?" I asked.

Mr. Griffin sat on his desk. "Ever heard of Andrew Carnegie?"

"As in Carnegie Hall?" Christy asked.

"Wasn't he a Robber Baron?" I asked.

"You're both right. He started out as a penniless immigrant, working twelve hour days for $1.20 a week. He worked his way up to become one of the wealthiest men in the world, then spent the latter portion of his life giving most of it away. He built Carnegie Hall as well as countless libraries around the world."

"What does he have to do with this Napoleon guy?" Darnell asked.

"Carnegie gave the young Napoleon Hill a task, and Hill spent the next 25 years completing it."

"What was the task?" I asked.

"To study the elements of success."

"So he studied successful people?" I asked.

"Not only. It wasn't enough to find commonalities among the successful. He also had to find what distinguished them from those he deemed failures."

"Those notecards you read," Jarod nodded to the cards next to Mr. Griffin. "They come from him?"

"They're my own practice, but I developed them by applying the principles I learned from Napoleon Hill."

"Let me guess," Jarod kicked his desk extra hard. "You want to fix our goals, and then I suppose you'll have us write them down on notecards?"

Mr. Griffin grinned like the Cheshire cat. "No, I want *you* to fix your goals." He leaned in toward Jarod. "We'll go over the steps of creating truly compelling goals for your life, as well as how to reinforce them so that they stick. That's where the notecards come in."

"How do they work?" Darnell asked. Was he actually excited by this?

"There are three components of the Outcome Cards. The first is your goal, the second is your deadline, and the third is the list of steps you'll take to hit that goal."

"Can you give us an example?" Darnell asked again.

"Certainly." Mr. Griffin picked up his stack of notecards, pulled one out and read:

> I intend to bring my marathon time down to three hours and fifteen minutes or below by April 16, in time for the Boston Marathon. To do this, I will 1) run at least four days per week, 2) run at least a half-marathon distance every Sunday, 3) weight train on my non-running days, 4) reward myself each time I break my fastest time, and 5) book additional training sessions with my coach whenever my average time drops.

"You run marathons?" Christy asked.

"I'm starting to. I want to compete in Ironman as well, but one thing at a time."

"So you're just supposed to let this piece of paper dictate what you do?" Jarod asked.

Mr. Griffin walked straight to Jarod's desk and slapped his notecard down on it. "Who wrote the note, Jarod?"

"I guess you did."

"And who developed the steps on the card?"

"Looks like the same handwriting to me…"

"Good to see you're paying attention," Mr. Griffin said. "So, who is dictating to whom?"

"I get your point, but still…." Jarod flicked his hand in the air. "It's like school—just having to follow more directions. Why should you have a notecard at all? Can't you just do what you want without it?"

"Yes, but I'm hardly consistent. Some days I want one thing, other days it's something else. That's why most people make such little progress in their lives. They never build momentum."

"This is ludicrous," Christy said. "Say one day I think I want to study law, and the next day I change my mind to medicine. You're saying that because I wrote law down on the notecard that I should stick with it?"

"Truthfully Christy, how often do you waffle between two burning desires?"

Christy shifted in her chair. "It happens sometimes."

"If you have even one burning desire, you're well ahead of the pack. Most people simply focus on getting through the day, the week, the semester, or whatever it is. To use your example, you'd be more likely to waffle between a vague idea that you'd sort of like to study law and another vague idea that you kinda think medicine would be better."

Jarod picked up Mr. Griffin's card and flapped it back and forth before him. "And these notecards are supposed to change that?"

"Absolutely. The present moment is like twilight. The past behind you is bright and clear, but the future ahead is a masked in darkness. Making an Outcome Card is like shining a beam of light into that darkness."

"You're telling me this card is going to predict my future?" Jarod asked.

"Your future is not set—there are infinite possibilities before you. The card helps you hone in on the future you choose to pursue."

"What if we make the card at the wrong time?" Darnell asked.

"What do you mean, the wrong time?"

"Well, like Christy said, sometimes you want law, other times medicine. What if you make the notecard during a time when you're thinking law, but you're better suited to medicine?"

"Excellent question, Darnell. That's why we make the cards during times of clarity."

"Like when?" Christy asked.

"Clarity most often comes at the extremes: when you're on top of the world and want to stay there, or when you hit rock bottom and want to pick yourself up. The problem is that these moments are fleeting."

"So we make the cards to remind us of the goals we made during those times of clarity?" I asked.

"Exactly. Then they keep us on track during the blah moments. For me, sometimes I want to train for the marathon; other times I'd rather sit on the couch with a beer and watch football. The notecards may be my voice, but they're my voice of vision. Any time that I think of skipping my workout, I read my card, and it's like my higher-self whispering in my ear."

"But isn't it possible," I asked, "that you can have a moment of clarity and still be wrong? Can't you have a rock bottom moment, say when you're struggling in biology, and suddenly see that it would be so much better to study law. What happens if you make my notecard and law isn't for you after all? Maybe you're best off sticking it through with medicine, or switching to engineering?"

"The notecards help you clarify that as well. Just because you write them doesn't mean that you're stuck with them for life. When I read my cards, I normally hear the voice of my higher-self. I know the goals on my card are what I want, and reading them helps me to refocus my energy. But periodically, when I read a card the goal doesn't move me at all. I don't hear the voice of my higher-self, I hear only delusion."

"What do you do then?" Christy asked.

"I tear up the card."

Christy's brow creased. She'd never given up on anything. "Just like that?"

"Normally I'll wait a day or two to make sure the feeling is consistent. Otherwise, I'd be in danger of trashing all my goals every time I get into a bad mood. But if nothing shifts, I tear it up."

Darnell picked at his cuticles, something he usually did during tests. "So if you keep not liking what the card says, you know you've set the wrong goal?"

"Or the wrong steps or the wrong date. Once you learn how to interpret your emotional reactions, they'll guide you toward your true goals as well as the ideal path to manifest them."

* * *

The next day, we rehashed our questions from the day before, even though we knew the answers. I wasn't the only one still trying to get my head around the concept. One thing that had become clear, Mr. Griffin said, "is that you guys aren't ready to work on a greater vision for your lives. At this point, it's best to choose one small goal to focus on."

Late in the class, Jarod raised his hand. "Mr. Griffin, perhaps if there were some grade incentives tied to the cards it would help us try them out."

"Grade incentives?" Mr. Griffin asked.

Darnell perked up. "Yeah, like if we got an automatic A in math if we made these cards and stuck to them."

Mr. Griffin raised his eyebrows. "For the opportunity to help you get your life on track, I have to give you an automatic A?"

Jarod said, "It doesn't have to be an A. but an incentive would certainly help us stick to it."

The bell rang. "I'll think your idea over, Jarod. See you all tomorrow."

"Remind me, what were we talking about yesterday?" Mr. Griffin asked with a grin as we took our seats the next day.

"Grade incentives," Jarod said. "You said you'd think them over."

"And I did. Do you really feel that an incentive would help you make and stick to the cards?"

"Yes," Jarod said.

"Does everyone feel this way?"

The rest of us said, "Yes."

"It's not enough to just read them in math class. The most important times to read your cards are first thing in the morning to set your intentions for the day, and immediately before bed, so they truly penetrate your unconscious mind. To see their effectiveness, you'll have to commit to doing this for at least 30 days. Are you all willing to do that?"

We all said, "Yes."

"The problem is, how will I know if you've done them? If there's a grade incentive, then there's also an incentive to lie."

"We can use an app," I suggested. "Each time we read our card, we check off the app. You'll get a notice with the time we did it."

"Interesting idea, Kelvin, but what if one of you claims you read the card but forgot to check off the app?"

Christy said, "We can put a note on the bottom of our cards saying 'check off the app.' Then if there's no check on the app, you'll know we didn't do it."

"Does everyone agree that if the app does not report that you read off the card, you won't get credit for reading it that time?" Mr. Griffin asked.

We agreed.

"Very well. I found an app that would work last night. I'll send you the link after class."

"Wait," I said. "You already thought about an app?"

"Once you brought up grade incentives, it made sense to have a way to keep track."

"Then why didn't you tell us about it?"

"I'm not here to give you answers, but to help you work them out. Didn't it feel better to come up with the solution on your own?"

I was annoyed at his ploy but had to admit that it had felt good when I made the suggestion. "I suppose great minds think alike."

"In my experience, it's the opposite," Mr. Griffin said. "Extraordinary minds are original. Ordinary minds think alike. Or perhaps I should say that those who don't actively grow their minds think alike, for every human mind can be extraordinary."

Was he calling me ordinary? Or insinuating that I wasn't growing my mind?

"Does this mean you'll do the grade incentives?" Jarod asked.

"I'm willing to give them a shot. But on two conditions. One, I'm only going to offer them to those students who genuinely feel the grade incentives will help them. Intrinsic motivation always trumps incentives in my mind. But I will give it as a tool for those who need it. How many of you feel you need this?"

At this point, I was already curious to try out the cards. While I understood his point about intrinsic motivation, I wasn't dumb enough to turn down a grade incentive. I eagerly raised my hand with the rest of the class.

"Fine. It can apply to all of you. Second, I will only do it for students who will commit, right now, that once you have a card, you will read it twice a day for 30 days. Even though you don't have your cards yet, once you commit, there is no backing out. Whoever doesn't wish to commit can still participate at their own pace, but will not qualify for the grade incentives. Who is ready to commit right now?"

Again, all of us raised our hands.

"Very well, then I have a contract for you all to sign. Get in line and sign one by one."

Mr. Griffin brought out a bunch of papers from his desk. "I've already signed my name and dated these. You just need to sign and print your names below."

The pages he held were full of text, written in what looked like 8 point font.

Darnell got up to the desk first and signed his name in the tiny space between the end of the text and the bottom of the page. I was next. The text began, "This is a contract between Mr. Griffin (herein "Mr. Griffin" or "teacher") and the students in his fifth-period trigonometry class (herein "student" or "students")…"

It would take me a full ten minutes to read the entire thing; maybe more, as it seemed all written in legalese. Sensing Jarod's impatience behind me, I quickly signed my name at the bottom as Darnell had. Neither Jarod nor Christy wasted their time with even trying to read over the text, just signed and returned to their seats.

Darnell seemed particularly pleased. "This is going to be the easiest math class ever! I can't believe I get an A for just reading this notecard twice a day."

"An A?" Mr. Griffin placed the signed contracts in a drawer, locked it, and dropped the key in his pocket. "That wasn't the agreement."

"Sure it was," Darnell said. "We talked about it yesterday."

"You suggested that yesterday. But the grade incentives weren't your idea—they were Jarod's. He was clear that the incentive didn't have to be an automatic A."

"So I'll still have to study math?" Darnell asked. "Bummer. But at least it should help. What do I get, another ten points on my average or something?"

"You don't get anything, Darnell. You lose points if you don't follow through."

"Lose points?" Jarod said. "That wasn't our deal."

"Of course it was. It was written very clearly on the contract you all signed."

"But we didn't even read the contracts."

"I noticed. Would you like to read them now?" Mr. Griffin handed around unsigned contracts, keeping the signed ones safely locked in his desk.

"Wait." Christy's eyes bulged over her copy. "I lose five points on my overall grade every time I forget to read my card?"

"Even if you remember to read the card, but forget to check the app," Mr. Griffin said. "Remember, that was your suggestion."

Heat rose to my cheeks. "If we forget more than five times we fail math?"

"Correct. Remember, I only gave this option to those who asked for a grade incentive. I always prefer intrinsic motivation. But you thought this would help you, so I offered it as a tool."

"A tool?" I said. "It sounds more like a punishment."

"Punishments, or the threat of them, can be great tools. You're all old enough to drive. How many of you try to stay within the speed limit?"

Silence.

"How many of you regularly go more than 20 miles per hour over the speed limit?"

Jarod raised his hand.

"The rest of you, what keeps you from driving that fast?"

"Over 20 miles an hour the tickets are like $160," Christy said.

"Yeah," Darnell said, "and my dad would take away my driving privileges if he ever caught me going that fast."

"None of you reduce your speed out of concern for safety?" Mr. Griffin asked.

No one responded.

"Teenagers." Mr. Griffin shook his head. "Do you see why society holds the threat of punishment over your heads? That's how they keep the roads safe."

A teacher intentionally tricking us into signing an agreement not in our interests? Who does this guy think he is? "I don't think it was fair putting it on the contract and not telling us," I said.

"Kelvin, do you remember what I told you my goals were for this year?"

I clenched my jaw and mumbled, "Something about helping us lead extraordinary lives."

"Precisely. Fairness was not among my goals."

We all groaned.

"Let this be a lesson to you. You must think hard about what you put on your cards because they'll give you laser focus toward these goals. Elements left off of your cards can get squeezed out." Mr. Griffin sat back on his desk. "Like fairness in my case."

"So now we're stuck?" Darnell asked.

"No, you're not stuck."

Darnell sat straighter. "You mean you'll let us take the contracts back?"

"No. That's another lesson I wanted to teach in a way that you'd never forget. You'll each sign hundreds, if not thousands of contracts in your life. Those who give them to you will primarily be looking out for their interests, not yours. Always be aware of what you bind yourself to."

Darnell's eyebrows pinched. "But you said we're not stuck?"

"You're not. You're welcome to transfer to another math class or drop math altogether. It all goes back to your vision for your life, and who you think can best help you get there. Care to transfer, Darnell?"

Darnell exhaled loudly. "No, I'll stay here."

"Anyone else?"

So far, I really couldn't say that I *liked* Mr. Griffin—he was like a mosquito that kept buzzing in my ear. Yet, he was intriguing. I doubted he'd ever bring us to the profound life transformations he promised, but no other teacher had ever attempted to. And...what if he did? Images of my nightmare in the cubicle wafted through my mind. My future vision could use some refining. It was worth a shot.

When no one said they wanted to transfer, Mr. Griffin said, "Just remember that you're not trapped. You're choosing to stay here."

"I still feel stuck to this contract," Darnell said.

"Yes, I know. It's written in your posture. The more ownership you take over your decisions, the straighter you'll sit in your chair. Besides, being stuck is not the worst thing. Sometimes I intentionally get myself stuck."

"Why would you do that?" I asked.

"I do it for motivation, and to force myself to find new answers."

"How can getting stuck motivate you?" Christy asked.

"It's like when Cortez burnt his ships upon landing in Mexico in 1519. The message to his men was clear. You can't back out. Succeed or die. I've used that technique on myself, though with less dire consequences."

"Like when?" Christy asked.

"I used it in college when trying to lose weight."

Darnell's head tilted up. "You, lose weight?" He scanned our lean, muscular teacher with cold eyes.

"You might not guess it looking at me now," Mr. Griffin patted his stomach, "but I used to be over 100 pounds overweight."

"Really?" Darnell was easily that overweight himself. "How did you lose it?"

"I tried diet after diet. I must have lost the same five pounds ten times, but I always put them right back on."

"So how'd you keep them off?"

"I backed myself into a corner. I made sure that I had two options, weight loss or a fate far worse than hunger."

"Like what?" Darnell asked.

"I made a list of all the foods I knew I needed to avoid, and I gave a copy of the list to all of my friends, plus a few people who were anything but my friends. I told them all that if they caught me eating anything on that list, they could make me eat whatever they wanted."

"Anything?"

"Anything that wouldn't injure or kill me. One day I was walking with my friend Andres, and we passed some fresh dog poop on the ground next to a hamburger stand. Andres asked them for a paper plate and a spoon, and scooped the poop onto the plate." Mr. Griffin cringed. "He waved it in front of me, telling me how much fun he was going to have watching me eat it all."

"Gross!" Jarod pretended to puke behind his desk.

"You never did, did you?" Christy asked.

"No. I lost the pounds, and Andres wound up with stale dog poop in his fridge. A couple of times I came close to cheating, and each time all I had to do was think of that plate of dog poop. Just knowing it was there, waiting for me, was enough to keep me on my diet."

The bell rang.

"I trust you've all had a memorable day. Next week we'll start working on your cards. And don't worry. The 30 days haven't even started yet."

"When do they start?" Christy asked.

"Everything will be just like it says on your contract."

"Where?"

Mr. Griffin's smirk returned. "On the other part you didn't read."

Chapter Three

Sink or Swim

I was curled up on the couch reading *The Martian* and trying to avoid thinking about Mr. Griffin and his sleazy contract when Dad walked in. He wore the same old khaki pants and a wrinkled button-down shirt. At least he didn't have acne anymore, though the pockmarks on his face showed that his skin had looked just like mine back in the day.

"Hi Kelvin," he said.

I didn't even look up. "Hey."

"How was school?"

"Fine."

"Liking the new math teacher any more?"

I didn't want to go there. "Eh."

"So...a physicist from London is lecturing at the university about black holes next Friday evening. Want to go?"

While half the senior class was at some party? "Nah."

"You'll be sure to get sucked in."

It took all my strength not to roll my eyes.

"I don't need to know until late in the week. You think about it until then, okay Kelvin?"

"Sure, Dad."

I felt him standing by the doorway, stalling. I guess Dad couldn't think of anything else to say, because after a minute, he continued on towards the kitchen.

* * *

"How about you, Christy. You have something you'd like to work on?"

It was Monday afternoon. Mr. Griffin just got through explaining the "rules." Each of us would start our 30 day period as soon as we chose our goal. He didn't want us to wait too long, or else we'd lose out on precious time. One goal immediately came to my mind, but there was no way I was going to discuss it in front of the class. When asked, I just lied and said I couldn't think of anything. Fortunately, Mr. Griffin moved on to Christy to find his first sucker.

"No, I don't have anything," Christy said.

"Nothing?"

"Nah. I had one, but I gave up on it."

"What was that?" Mr. Griffin asked.

"Last year, when coach appointed me captain of the girls' swim team, I made it my goal to win the State Championship this year."

"Why'd you give up on it?"

"You didn't hear what happened?"

Mr. Griffin rubbed his chin. "Was that the drunk driver?"

Christy nodded and tears collected in her eyes. "Coach was killed the week before school began."

"They haven't given you anyone else?"

"No." Christy shoved her hands into the narrow gap between her crossed legs. "I approached the athletic director, and he said he didn't have the time to get someone new. I learned later that they used most of the budget to get an extra assistant coach for the football team."

"Don't they legally have to give you a coach?"

"Yeah. There's this lady who works as a pool attendant who said she'd be willing to accompany us to meets, so he gave her a tiny salary and appointed her as our official coach. She doesn't do anything though."

"So who runs practice?"

"Jill and I. Jill is my co-captain. But we don't know what we're doing. The older girls aren't making any progress, and the younger ones are completely lost."

Mr. Griffin leaned on the edge of his desk. "Tell me about your coach."

"Coach Silver was amazing. When she made me captain and told me she wanted to win States this year, I actually thought we had a chance."

"And now?"

Christy shook her head. "Now we're hopeless."

Mr. Griffin swept his eyes over the entire class. "You get what you settle for."

Christy's eyes narrowed. "What does that mean?"

"You probably think that you gave up on your goal because it went out of reach. I expect it's the opposite: your goal left your reach because you gave up on it."

"Our coach died!" Christy's tears spilled down her cheeks. Why was Mr. Griffin being so heartless?

"Did you only want to win for the coach?" he asked.

Christy mumbled, "Of course not. For all of us."

"Then why give up just because you lost your coach?"

"We're not giving up. We're just hopeless." A new rush of anguish overcame her.

"*Hopeless*. An interesting choice of language. You didn't say you're incapable. After all, you have the same athletes on the team that you had before your coach died, so if you had the physical capabilities to win before, you've still got them now. As you point out, what's changed is your belief in yourselves. You no longer have hope."

"What's changed," Christy sat up straight and drove her words like daggers, "is that our coach is dead! We're lost without her."

Mr. Griffin kept his cool. "I'm not saying that your path is without challenges. But after all, there's little thrill in achieving easy victories. My goal is to stretch you, to show you that you're capable of achieving so much more than you realize."

"I know what the team is capable of, Mr. Griffin, and the championship is beyond us."

Mr. Griffin sighed and went to the whiteboard. "I want you all to remember this quote." He wrote down:

The Size of your Dreams must always exceed
your current capacity to achieve them.

—Ellen Johnson Sirleaf

"Who is she?" Christy asked.

"The first woman ever elected President of an African nation. She also said, 'If your dreams do not scare you, they are not big enough.' She would know about scary dreams. Her efforts to end Liberia's cycle of violence and promote women's rights earned her a Nobel Peace Prize."

"Not all of us are looking to change the world, Mr. Griffin," Christy said.

"Big changes evolve from small changes, Christy. Today, we might only be working on a high school swim team, but you never know what challenge tomorrow brings. Master these tools now, and you'll be prepared to face whatever lies ahead."

Christy sank into her chair and crossed her arms.

Mr. Griffin put down the whiteboard marker. "I know you're all deeply skeptical of my approach. Tell me, Christy, if following my steps leads you to win the State Championship, will I win you over to my methods?"

Christy's head bent to the side. "You serious?"

"You bet. If you won the Championship, would you trust me then?"

"Absolutely."

"I believe it's possible, but only if you're willing to try."

Christy shrugged her shoulders. "I'll try. Why not? You'll fail me anyhow if I don't."

"No, not like that. I'm not talking about putting a toe in the water. I'm talking about going all in, giving me everything you've got."

"I thought you said this was going to only be five minutes a day for 30 days?"

"That's right, your homework from me will only be five minutes a day for 30 days, but I need your complete dedication during those five minutes. Plus, you'll give yourself additional tasks to complete *your* goal. You'll need to put the same dedication into those. Agreed?"

"Okay, I guess."

"This is not a guessing game, Christy. Remember, you get what you settle for. Winning is going to take more dedication than that."

She wiped her eyes with the back of her hands. "I'm dedicated."

Mr. Griffin shook his head. "I don't know. I'm not seeing a girl who's passionate about winning the State Championship."

"What?" Christy slapped her hand against her desk. "How can you say that?"

"You think you have the passion it takes?"

"Absolutely."

"Then if you have the passion and the dedication, come up here."

Christy stepped up to the front of the room.

"Face the class and close your eyes. Go on, no one's going to laugh at you. Good. Now ask yourself, what would it mean to you to lead your team to victory in the State Championship?"

"It would be great."

"Just great? I want you to imagine that you've made it to the Championship and it's neck and neck. What's the last event?"

"The 4 x 100 relay."

"What place are you swimming?"

"Last, I'm the anchor."

"Excellent. So you're standing on the edge of the pool, waiting your turn. The girls on your team are good, but the competition is better. To your left and right, the anchors from the other teams jump into the pool. Finally, your teammate hits the edge of the pool, and you jump in. You're behind, but determined. By the time you finish your first lap, you've caught up to all but two of the swimmers. 50 yards to go. You're halfway through the second lap when you pass the next girl. 25 yards. You're tired. Your arms are burning. But nothing's going to stop you. You draw strength from deep down. 15 yards. She's still ahead. 10 yards. You're getting close. 5 yards. You've pulled even. You reach out and, by a finger's breath, hit the edge of the pool first.

"Can you see it, Christy?"

Christy nodded.

"Can you feel it, Christy?"

"Yes."

"What happens next?"

"The entire team goes crazy. They all jump into the pool and hug me. We're all screaming, some even crying." Christy's eyes swelled.

Mr. Griffin said, "You barely have time to towel off before someone hands you the largest trophy you've ever seen and a microphone. What do you say?"

"I'd take the trophy over to the stands."

"Why? Who's in the stands?"

"Coach Silver's nine-year-old daughter Kim is there, watching with her dad. I'd say, 'we want you to have this, Kim, from all the girls on the team. Whenever you look at it, we want you to remember everything your mom did for us. Without her, we never could have won. And remember all that she did for you. You didn't have her long enough. But with the gifts she gave you, you can do anything!'"

"I want everyone to remember this look on Christy's face. That's the look of inspiration. With the expression she had ten minutes ago, she was barely capable of achieving the ordinary. With this look, she's ready to take on the *extraordinary*. Christy, make the sound of victory you're feeling right now."

Christy raised her eyebrows and shook her head.

"Come now, Christy. You told me you were fully dedicated."

She turned away and wiped her eyes.

Mr. Griffin faced us. "One reason that so few people achieve the extraordinary is that we get embarrassed by the power of our own greatness. Don't let Christy fall into that trap. If you believe in her, let her know."

Jarod, who never minded making an ass of himself in class, pumped his fist and started chanting, "Christy! Christy!"

Darnell and I looked at each other. I shrugged and joined in. Darnell threw his fist in the air. Ordinarily, teachers quieted us down when we started getting too rowdy, but Mr. Griffin screamed, "Louder!"

"Christy! Christy!"

"Don't let her stand there alone. If you believe in her, get on your feet."

Jarod was the first to rise. This math class was finally jiving with him. Once he was up, Darnell and I also stood up. "Christy! Christy!"

"You see, Christy," Mr. Griffin said, "you can't embarrass yourself in front of them. They're all behind you. They all believe in you. Now, let me hear the sound of victory."

Christy thrust her arms high, "Yeah!"

"Do it again. Louder"

"Yeaaaaaaaaah!"

"Once again, but this time, I want everyone who believes in Christy to join in. Go!"

We all shouted. Jarod took her in a bear hug. When he let go, Darnell stepped forward, with arms halfway out, then backed off, hovering just beyond her reach.

"Now stop," Mr. Griffin said.

The class grew quiet.

"Everyone take your seats. That was the easy part."

Easy?

"Tell me, Christy, what would you do to make that vision a reality?"

"Anything."

"Anything? Be careful what you commit to. To get you there, we may have to put that 'anything' to the test."

Christy nodded. "What do I do now?"

"First, take a notecard. You're going to create what I call an Outcome Card." Mr. Griffin handed her one from his desk. "Write on the top:

___I intend to captain the girls' swim team to Victory in the State Championship on . . .___

"When's the championship?"

"March 8th."

___I intend to captain the girls' swim team to victory in the State Championships on March 8th. To accomplish this, I will do the following:___

32

"Got it," Christy looked up. "What do I write next?"

"I have no idea," Mr. Griffin said.

"That's all that goes on the card?"

"No. You need to write down the steps you'll take."

"What are the steps?" Christy asked.

"How should I know?" Mr. Griffin shrugged. "I don't know what it takes to win at swimming. I can't even do the backstroke."

"You don't know? So we've done all of this for nothing?"

"Hardly for nothing. Tell me what you need to do."

Christy slumped in her chair. "I don't know."

"I think you know far more than you're letting on. And if you're truly stuck, I bet you can find others willing to lend you a hand."

Turning to the class, he said, "Raise your hand if you're willing to help Christy find the answers she needs."

All of us raised our hands.

Turning back to Christy, he said, "I'll help too. Just don't expect others to have the answers for you. You'll get plenty of suggestions, probably more than you can handle, but the ultimate decision has to rest with you. Understand?"

Christy nodded.

"Now, tell me one thing you need to do to captain your team to the Championship."

Christy bit the end of her pen. "Get a decent coach I guess."

"I'm not sure a decent coach will cut it at this point, are you?"

Christy sat straighter. "No. To save us, we need an amazing coach."

"Excellent, so now add to your card:

1. Find an amazing coach

Christy wrote it down. "But how do I do that? We don't even have the budget to hire one."

"True. Since this is such an important step, and since it will have a distinct timeline and its own collection of steps, I think it merits a notecard of its own." Mr. Griffin handed her another card. "This time, write at the top:

I intend to find an amazing coach for the girls swim team by . . .

"When do you need the coach by?" Mr. Griffin asked.

"We need her already."

"How long can you give it?"

Christy thought for a moment. "I'd say no more than two weeks."

"Then write:

I intend to find an amazing coach for the girls' swim team by November 24. To accomplish this, I will do the following steps.

"Now we're back where we started," Christy said. "I don't know what to put down."

"As you were brave enough to go first, I'm going to help you with this card. You yourself said that a good coach just won't cut it. You need an amazing coach. Tell me, who are the best swimming coaches in the world?"

"I don't know. I suppose the Olympics coaches. Or the coaches of the top college programs."

"Excellent. Start with them."

Christy shot up in her chair. "I can't do that!"

"Why not?"

"What do you want me to do, call the Russian Olympics coach and tell her I'm a high school student looking for a swim coach, and oh yeah, I have no budget to pay you, but would you help me out by coaching me for free?"

"I'd be inclined to start with the US Olympics coach rather than the Russian, but why not? Worst case, you'll get a no, which leaves you no worse off than you are now."

"I'm guaranteed to get a no, so why bother wasting my time?"

"Granted, if you call her up and yap like a whiny teenager, 'I'm looking for a coach who's willing to work for free,' then you'll get a no."

"So what do I say?"

"Don't tell her what you want her to do, tell her why you want her to do it."

Christy brow pinched. "I want her to do it because we need a coach."

"No, that's still what you *want her to do*." Mr. Griffin groaned. "You need to sell her on your vision."

Christy tilted her head. "How do I do that?"

"Tell me, why do you need a coach?" Mr. Griffin tapped his pen against his palm.

"So we can win."

"And what will you do if you win?"

"Dedicate the victory to Coach Silver's memory."

"Why?"

"She was an amazing coach and got killed by a drunk driver." Christy pursed her lips. "We miss her."

"That" Mr. Griffin pointed his pen at her, "is a lot more compelling than 'we want a coach for free.'"

"Yeah," Jarod said, "when you first said you wanted a new coach, I didn't care all that much. But when you stood in front of the class and dreamed up your win at State's, I got all excited for you."

Christy turned to face him. "Really?"

"For sure."

"So," Mr. Griffin said, "now can you think of what you could say to a top coach?"

"I guess I could tell her about Coach Silver and how she was killed and how we want to win State's and dedicate the win in her memory."

Jarod added, "Even I'd coach your team if you talked to me like that."

Christy smacked him on the side of the head. "You can barely even float."

"You have a powerful vision, Christy," Mr. Griffin said. "It's my experience that the best coaches love their sport and love helping others improve. Throw in a good cause, and I think you'll be surprised at how willing they'll be to help."

"That doesn't mean she'd move here from Russia to coach us," Christy said.

"Still on the Russian Olympics coach?" Mr. Griffin asked. "No, she won't move here to work with you. But you've defined success too narrowly. If you're looking for one of these coaches to quit their job and coach you instead, you're dreaming."

"But I need a coach." Christy turned her hands up. "How else could I define success?"

"Class, any of you have any thoughts?"

"I think," Darnell said, "that you could ask them if there's any help they'd be willing to give, even if it's not actually coaching you. Maybe they could give you tips or something."

"We need more than just advice at this point."

"Of course you do," Mr. Griffin said, "but Darnell's right. You don't need to get everything on the first call. The Russian Olympics coach is connected to top coaches all over the world, including some who live several thousand miles closer. She might be willing to make an introduction or even look at a video of one of your practices and give you feedback over video conference."

"You really think she'd say yes?"

"Absolutely," Mr. Griffin said. "I think there's at least a 10% chance."

Whatever light had built up in Christy's eyes went out. "Only 10%? So now we're back to nowhere."

"Not even close. Tell me, what separates great salespeople from ordinary ones?"

Christy shrugged. "I suppose it's the ability to get people to say yes."

"That's the second greatest distinction. More important is the ability to hear the word no."

"How does that help?" Jarod asked.

"Ordinary salespeople go out on a sales call, and if they get a no, they get discouraged. The great ones hear no after no and keep going. Some even tell themselves that they need to hear no ten times to get one yes. Getting a no actually excites them, as they tell themselves that it brings them closer and closer to getting a yes."

"What are you saying?" Christy asked.

"Like I told you before, each time you reach a world class coach and tell her your story, you might have a 10% chance of getting her to help you out. So if you're only willing to call one or two coaches, the odds are that you'll fail. But remember, this is a math class. What would happen to your odds if you called 20?"

"Now you want me to call 20 of the best coaches in the world?"

"A few minutes ago, when I asked you what you'd be willing to do to reach your goal, you said *anything*. Now you're telling me that making 20 phone calls is beyond you?"

"I guess not."

"Good. So on your second notecard, write down the following steps:

1. Research the top swimming coaches in the world
2. Make a list of 20 World Class Coaches to reach out to

"But here's the thing, if you call with the expectation of getting a no, they'll detect that in your voice. Before each call, you must reconnect with your vision and fully believe that you'll get a yes."

"That makes sense to me," Christy said. "Coach Silver always told us that no matter how strong our competition, we could never go into a race thinking we were going to lose."

"Excellent, then add to your card:

3. Before each call, I will reconnect with my vision and get myself into a peak state

"Peak state?"

"Yes, in an excited, high energy, positive state of being. When you're in a peak state, it's contagious. Let's add one more:

4. Call each coach, and be open to whatever help they offer to give

"Are you willing to do all of that?"

"Yes, Mr. Griffin."

"If you do all of that, I expect that before your two-week deadline you'll have the coaching you need. Remember to read your cards every morning and night and check off the app each time. Your 30-day commitment starts now."

The bell rang.

"Remember, all of you committed to help Christy. Homework for tonight, I want everyone researching the world's top swimming coaches. Names are good, but let's not settle for good. Go the extra mile and get Christy phone numbers as well."

* * *

The rest of the day, I couldn't get that class out of my mind. At first, Mr. Griffin had seemed like an insensitive jerk. Rather than sympathizing with Christy's situation, he attacked her. I'd done that plenty of times myself, yelling at people when I thought they were doing the wrong thing, and it only resulted in a blowup. I learned that if I wanted people to respond to me, I was better off being sympathetic. Yet, despite his attacks, Christy had shifted, and even I believed that she might be able to find herself a coach now. How had he done that?

As soon as I got home, I created a new Google Sheet entitled _The World's Top Swimming Coaches_. I immediately invited Christy, Jarod, and Darnell and gave them editorial access to the spreadsheet. Then, after a moment, I added Mr. Griffin as well. Why not? He said he'd help.

Getting a list of the top college coaches would be easy. I could download the college rankings from the past few years and look into their programs. Perhaps I'd do that if I had time. For now, I wanted to set my sights a bit higher.

After an hour and a half of work, and plenty of help from Google Translate, I managed to find not only my target's mobile phone number but her home number and email as well. I sat back and admired my work, picturing the expression on Christy's face when she saw the contact information for the Russian Olympics coach.

Chapter Four

Mastermind

The next day math was canceled for a school assembly. On Wednesday, Christy walked into class with a noticeable bounce in her step.

"Something tells me you have news to report," Mr. Griffin said.

"My classmates went a bit over the top in the coaching hunt. I now have 36 contacts."

Actually, I was the only one of her classmates that added anything to the list. I had entered 23 of the names, and Christy had done the remaining 13 on her own.

"Have you called any yet?" Mr. Griffin asked.

"Six."

"How were the responses?"

"The first five were all no's. One was kind of a jerk, but the other four were all sweet and apologetic. One was adamant that I could do it myself and recommended that I read the book *The Talent Code* to learn more about coaching. You'll never guess which coach that was."

"The Russian Olympics coach?" Mr. Griffin asked.

"You got it." Christy winked in my direction. "Then last night, I got my first partial yes."

"Tell us."

"I called the coach of State College, Jan Morgan. They finished twelfth in the country last year. Coach Jan invited us to come down for a joint practice on Friday." Christy bounced in her seat. "Their practice facility is only a half hour from here."

"Great first step. How about the rest of your list?"

"I have to keep calling them, don't I? One joint practice is hardly going to get us to win the State Championship."

"Any other updates?"

"Yes, I've been working with my co-captain Jill on our plan. We added two more items to my first notecard. Now it reads:

I intend to captain the girls' swim team to victory in the State Championships on March 8th. To accomplish this, I will do the following:

1. Find an Amazing coach
2. Unite all the girls on the team with our vision of victory
3. Work on my coaching skills

Mr. Griffin tipped an imaginary hat to Christy. "Any changes to your coaching card?"

"We added one more step there:

I intend to find an amazing coach for the girls swim team by November 24. To accomplish this, I will do the following steps.

1. Research the top swimming coaches in the world
2. Make a list of 20 World Class Coaches to reach out to
3. Before each call, I will reconnect with my vision and get myself in a peak state of mind.
4. Call each coach, and be open to whatever help they offer to give.
5. Create a Team Video showing who we are and why we want to win so badly

"A video...interesting." His eyes sparkled. "Why'd you add that?"

"Like you said, great coaches know each other. But just knowing another coach isn't enough, they need to be able to tell our story, to convey why it's worth helping us out. With a video, we can make the case for ourselves, and give these coaches something they can easily pass on."

"Great thinking. When do you plan to make the video?"

"I only came up with the idea while reading my cards this morning. I'd like to do it at practice today, though I don't yet have a plan for how." Christy looked around the room. "You all said you'd help. Any of you know how to make a video?"

Her eyes skimmed over Jarod and Darnell, then came to rest on me. She knew, as we all did, that I was the only one of us experienced in video editing, let alone had the software to do it. She gave me a beseeching smile I couldn't resist.

"I can edit it tonight with Final Cut," I said. "Can you shoot it today?"

"I need to be running practice," she said. "Could you come and shoot it too?"

I dropped my eyes. "You'd want me there?"

"Of course." The sound of pity in her voice made me sink lower in my chair. "I'd love your help."

"OK," I said, without looking up. "I'll come shoot it too."

"Thank you. And stop blushing. We'll be in swim suits, not naked."

Note: if you ever want someone to stop blushing, don't point it out in public. I buried my face in my hands as Jarod and Darnell enjoyed a good laugh.

"That's wonderful news about the joint practice," Mr. Griffin said again, probably just to draw the attention off of me.

Christy beamed. "A bonus is that they're also one of my top choices for college next year. Even if they don't offer us any additional assistance this year, if I make a strong enough impression at the practice, it might help my chances of getting an athletic scholarship."

"It might indeed. One thing I love about doing this work is that once you start building momentum down your path, you never know what additional doors will open up."

A "humph" came from the back of the room.

"Yes, Jarod. You have something to add?"

"No, I'm good." Jarod crossed his arms and turned his head away.

"You don't sound so *good*," Mr. Griffin said.

"Just bitter and jealous. Let's not make a big deal out of it."

"Too late for that. Bitter about what?"

"I don't want to give Christy a hard time. It's not her fault."

"What isn't?" Mr. Griffin asked.

"That she might have a chance for a scholarship to State. Christy's a friend—I want her to get it. I'm just jealous because I might go there too, but unlike her, I have no idea how I'm supposed to pay for it."

"Why not take out loans?" Darnell asked.

"And work the rest of my life just to pay them off? Should I be like my step-brother Mike who turned 30 last month and hasn't even paid off half of his college loans? At the rate he's going, it'll take him another ten years just to be broke."

"Thank you for volunteering to be the next victim in our experiment." Mr. Griffin strolled over to Jarod's desk, a blank notecard in hand.

"No thanks, Mr. Griffin. I'll pass."

"I don't think so." Mr. Griffin pointed right at him. "Let's not forget that you were the one who asked for the grade pressure to help you along. You've signed a contract allowing me to invoke a 30 day period whenever I want requiring you to read your cards every morning and night. No card, no credit for reading it."

Jarod huffed.

"As I recall, you need this math credit to graduate. Wasn't that your reason for taking the class? Now, what would you like to accomplish in these next 30 days?"

"Nothing."

"If you're feeling bitter and jealous, there's *something* you want."

"I was feeling jealous at the idea that Christy can get herself a scholarship and bitter because I know I can't get one myself, alright?"

"Why are you so certain you can't get a scholarship?"

"State only gives scholarships for sports and academics." Jarod's shoe jittered against the leg of his desk. "I don't play sports, and my grades are barely strong enough to get in."

"Do you have any idea how many millions of dollars of independent scholarships are available in this country? Many go unclaimed. You'd be surprised at what you might qualify for."

"Applying for scholarship after scholarship that I'm not going to get sounds like more pointless homework. Besides, it will take away time that I could be using to actually earn money for college."

"What do you do to earn money?" Mr. Griffin said.

"I mow a few lawns after school."

"You mow so many lawns that you have no extra time for applying for scholarships?"

"I told you already, scholarships are not for me."

"I understand. For the notecards to work, it's vital that the goal comes from you, not from me. What I'm focused on now is not the scholarships, it's the time. You mow so many lawns that you have so little available time?"

"No. I have time."

"How much will you make mowing this month?"

"Maybe $250."

"Could you mow more?"

"If there was enough business, I'd take it."

"How much do you need to make to go to college?"

"Without taking loans? In-state tuition is not too bad. I'll need about $20,000 a year to make it work with room and board."

"What about without room and board? Is living at home an option?"

Jarod shook his head. "Not a chance, Mr. Griffin. I'm moving out the first chance I get."

"Alright, $20,000 a year. Are you planning on working while in college?"

"I suppose I'll have to."

"And during the summers?"

"Of course. But that won't get me enough to cover my costs."

"How much do you need to have saved up before you're willing to start? Enough to pay for all four years?"

"No. One year's good enough for me. Who knows, I might not even like it when I get there. I'd go if I had $20,000 saved up."

"And how much do you have now?"

"$7000."

"School starts in nine months. That means you'll need to save around $1500 a month, correct?"

"You're the math teacher, Mr. Griffin."

Christy squeezed her lips to fight a laugh.

"Perhaps," Mr. Griffin said, "but this is less a question of math, and more a question of psychology. Rather than creating a nine-month goal of coming up with $13,000, we're going to create a goal for just the next month."

"So I'd need to jump from $250 a month to $1500? There's no way."

Mr. Griffin turned to the class. "I want everyone to pay attention to the tone of Jarod's voice. He's convinced that he'll never be able to hit a goal of $1500. Notecards are a potent tool when used right, but the fastest way to undermine their effectiveness is to choose a goal that you can't believe in. If every time you read it, you think, 'this is garbage, I'll never be able to do this,' then you're not building momentum, you're killing it."

"But that's how I feel."

"Exactly, so it's better to choose a less ambitious short-term goal that you can genuinely believe in. Hitting it will build your momentum, and inspire you to set a higher goal over the next period."

"It's gotta be way less than 1500 bucks."

"So you tell me, if you put all of your effort into mowing lawns the next month, what is the absolute highest amount you think you can make?"

"$750 perhaps. If I bust my butt, maybe $1000 at the very tops."

"$1000 it is. While I don't want a goal that you can't believe in, I want to stretch you to your limits. In truth, all of you are capable of so much more than you realize. So Jarod, here's a notecard. Write at the top:

> *I intend to mow $1000 worth of lawns between November 13 and December 13. To accomplish this, I will do the following:*

"Got it. But why the 13th? Today is only the 12th."

"I'm glad to hear the change in your voice and to see you're willing to go along. As a result, I've decided to give you a bit of a reprieve. With Christy, we needed to move quickly. With you, we have a little extra time to play with, so I'm going to delay starting your 30 day period to give you one more element of the process.

"For today, write nothing more. Your homework, Jarod, is to think of all the steps you can take to reach the $1000 goal in one month. I want the rest of you to do the same, to brainstorm any advice you can give Jarod to help him reach his goal."

* * *

I barely slept that night. The filming for Christy went well, far better than I thought. I don't know if it was because she introduced me, or because I was just the guy behind the camera, but the entire team accepted me right away.

I planned to video whatever Christy wanted me to record. But it became immediately clear that she had no idea what she wanted the video to look like, nor how to make a video go viral. Her co-captain Jill just shrugged, equally clueless.

I ventured a couple of suggestions, and they seemed happy to let me do what I wanted. No, not happy, *thrilled*.

"I'm so relieved you're here," Christy had said. I, of course, totally blushed again.

With half an hour left in practice, I'd already gotten all of the emotional shots done. I had more than enough film of the girls talking about their coach, talking about their vision. When everyone went along with my more conventional suggestions, I got a bit more bold, only to find that I got no pushback on those ideas either.

I spent the rest of the time taking fun shots, hoping to make the film entertaining enough that coaches would want to pass it on.

I finished the editing at 5 am. I left my computer to complete the rendering process and passed out for a couple of hours of well-deserved sleep.

* * *

"Whose idea was it to put arm floats on the freshmen?" Jarod asked. We all stood huddled around my laptop watching the completed video.

"Kelvin's. Of course." Christy shot me a bemused smile that I gratefully returned.

"I thought it would be a funny way of showing how they're struggling to bring the new girls along without a coach."

"Very clever," Mr. Griffin said. "The more viral the video, the easier time you'll have finding a coach. Have you sent it to anyone, Christy?"

"Not yet. Kelvin just finished it this morning. But I did speak to five more coaches yesterday. One actually called me back from a voicemail I'd left."

"Anyone else say yes?"

"Actually two more did. One asked me to video a practice and promised to send feedback."

"That's great. And the other?"

Christy puffed out her chest. "The coach of the US Olympic team took my call. He said he'd do whatever he could to help us out."

Jarod shook his head. "People always say stuff like that. Did he offer anything?"

Christy shoved her face in his. "Actually, Mr. Attitude Problem, he *did*. He's going to be in the area in January, and he offered to attend one of our practices."

"Fantastic," Mr. Griffin said. "The best coaches often teach more in a few hours than an average coach can teach in a year."

"There's more." Christy danced in her seat. "He told me to send him our video, and promised to send it around and post it on his Facebook page."

"Nicely done, Christy." Mr. Griffin high-fived her. "Now, if everyone will take their seats, I want to hear how you did on last night's homework."

"Homework?" Darnell asked.

"You were all supposed to brainstorm ways to help Jarod mow $1000 worth of lawns in the next month. What did you come up with?"

"I've actually been thinking about it," Jarod said, "and I've come up with a few ideas."

"Go, Jarod!" Christy said.

"I want to hear all of your ideas," Mr. Griffin said, "but not yet. First I want to hear from your classmates. Anyone?"

Silence filled the room.

"Nothing?" Mr. Griffin raised an eyebrow. "I'll admit I expected this group to take homework a bit more seriously. You did hear me give you all the assignment to brainstorm ideas for Jarod, did you not?"

I'd worked so hard on the swim team's video that this other assignment completely slipped my mind. I deliberately avoided looking at Jarod, but in the corner of my eye, I could see his head slump.

"Maybe he could call the 20 greatest mowers in the world?" Christy teased.

"Thanks a lot, Christy," Jarod replied.

"Sometimes even jokes contain wisdom," Mr. Griffin said. "There's hardly a profession on earth that doesn't have its failures and its millionaires. Many of those who today own multi-million dollar landscaping businesses started out just like you, mowing one lawn at a time. Joking or not, Christy is right that one of those people could almost certainly give you advice that would take you years to work out on your own. Anyone else?"

"On a more serious note," Christy said, "what if you printed out a flyer and put it in people's mailbox?"

"Actually," Jarod cut in, "I already—."

"Not yet, Jarod. I want you to listen first. Who else has an idea for Jarod?"

"What if you went around the neighborhood looking for homes with totally overgrown lawns?" Darnell said. "They might be more likely to hire you."

"Could be." Jarod made a note.

It would have been so easy last night to do a few Google searches on successful landscaping practices. Instead, I forgot all about it and let Jarod down. Why? What had gotten us all so excited about Christy's goal that was missing in Jarod's? Then it hit me. It was her *story*. The murdered coach, the dream of becoming champions. It was *compelling*.

"What about your story?" I asked.

"My story? I'm a guy who mows lawns."

"I know. But..." I closed my eyes and tried to find the right words. "It's like..."

"What?" Jarod demanded.

"Go on, Kelvin," Mr. Griffin said. "You've got something. Take as long as you need."

I got to my feet and began pacing, as if the desk was somehow constraining my thoughts. "Christy thought she was just a girl on a swim team looking for a coach. As Mr. Griffin said, if she called all of these famous coaches and said, 'do you know anyone willing to coach some girls for free?' they all would have laughed at her. But making the video, it occurred to me how much stronger her true story is. It's a story that when coaches hear it, they immediately want to help. I bet they can't help wonder what would happen to their own teams if they were suddenly killed. That's got to awaken something in them."

"It's a good story," Jarod said, "but how does it help *me*? I'm still just a guy who mows lawns."

"I know you are," I said, "but a week ago, Christy was just a girl who swims. The story was sitting there the whole time, but we couldn't see it. Mr. Griffin had to stick it in our face before any of us knew it was there. Could there be a great story lurking there for you too?"

"Like what?" The tension in Jarod's voice made me hesitate. He was not a guy I wanted to pick a fight with.

"I don't know. Maybe the fact that you want to mow lawns to go to college. Maybe people will feel better about paying you if they're not just thinking about their lawns, but also where the money will go?"

Jarod's foot jittered on the tiled floor, and he chewed the inside of his cheek. He was at least thinking over what I just said.

Out of words, I felt like an idiot standing up before the class, and quickly retook my seat.

"I'm glad you got that out, Kelvin," Mr. Griffin said. "There's more wisdom in your words than you realize." He paced up and down before the class. "Did anyone notice what just went on here?"

When no one responded, he continued, "Do any of you remember Napoleon Hill?"

"Wasn't he the notecard guy?" Jarod asked.

"No, I'm the notecard guy. But you're correct that the notecards rely on his discoveries of how to train your mind toward a goal. We just saw another one of his core principles in action, the Mastermind Group."

"Mastermind?" Christy asked. "Like the game?"

"No, Christy, not like the game. The concept of the Mastermind Group is to bring together others whose expertise and ideas complement your own."

"How can they compliment my ideas?" Jarod asked. "You didn't let me share them."

"Not compliment, complement, with an 'e,' which means to add to what you've done to enhance or improve it. I didn't let you share your ideas first because I knew how reluctant the class was to come forward. Had you shared first, I expect they would have simply deferred to your ideas, and been even less forthcoming with their own."

Mr. Griffin turned to the rest of us. "Let me emphasize: when you defer to the ideas of others, you do them no favors. Jarod may not choose to adopt any of your suggestions, but I guarantee that sharing your ideas activated his mind and got him thinking in ways he wouldn't have done on his own. Am I right, Jarod?"

"True."

"Now that you've heard them, you can decide which ideas you want to keep, eliminate, or synthesize with your own thoughts. Let's hear what you've come up with."

"One minute." Jarod scribbled on his card. "I'm making some quick changes."

"While Jarod finishes, let me make my intentions clear. From this point on, this class is your Mastermind Group. That doesn't mean your classmates are the only ones you can turn to for help. Feel free to seek additional guidance, as Christy is doing with her coaches. But it does mean you're expected to show up for one another. When a classmate shares an idea, don't just listen or even appreciate it. Look for flaws, alternative perspectives, opportunities missed. The best Mastermind partners are not gentle; they say what's on their mind, though ideally without mockery, Christy.

"If your idea is being torn apart, don't sit meekly and take it. If you think you're right, give reasons. If you hear a glint of wisdom but aren't sure you fully grasp it, hash it out until you own it. Those of you who work out know your muscles grow when they're challenged. Your brain works the same way."

"OK, I'm ready," Jarod said. "Here goes:

I intend to make $1000 between November 13 and December 13. To accomplish this, I will do the following:

1. Call all past customers who have not hired me in a while to see if they're again interested.
2. Print out a flyer and pass it around my neighborhood. The flyer will not only say that I mow lawns, rake leaves, shovel snow, etc., it will also say who I am and why I want the money.

"That second part I just added now." He nodded at me.

---

3. Keep my existing rate for customers willing to commit to one mow/lawn care per week, and raise my rate by $10 for one-offs.
4. Call people with successful landscaping businesses until I reach someone willing to give me advice.

"How do you feel about your list, Jarod?" Mr. Griffin asked.

"It feels good. I'm still not sure it will get me all the way to $1000, though."

"You're probably right. But it doesn't need to—not yet. How much do you think you can make putting this new plan into place?"

"I don't know. Maybe $600."

"You see the power here? You've only been working on this for one day, and you've already more than doubled your productivity.

"Reading the card, along with putting the steps into motion, will activate your mind. You'll begin to realize that some of these steps are more powerful than others. You'll reorder them, scratch some off, and develop better ideas to take their place. Commit to this process and I feel certain that your card a month from now will look little like it does now."

* * *

Derek Andrews' parents were out of town. Again. So, of course, he was having yet another party. And, of course, I wasn't invited. Still, I wasn't going to some lecture with Dad.

He ended up taking Mom on condition that they eat at her favorite Italian restaurant afterward. I stayed home to babysit Megan, who in all honesty was old enough to hire herself out as a babysitter. At least it was easy money. All I had to do was order pizza and let her watch whatever she wanted on Netflix, and she left me alone.

I found Napoleon Hill's book online and started reading it. It was kind of interesting in that century-ago-English sort of way. It got me thinking about the notecards. I looked at the crumpled cards piling up in my bedroom trash can. There was no way I could ever share any of those in class. Besides, my goal was not remotely realistic.

Hill's book dropped out of my hand, and I sank back into *The Martian*. Mark Watney might be freaking out, but I could think of worse fates than being stuck on a planet all by myself.

Chapter Five

Defining Moments

C hristy had news on Monday, but Mr. Griffin chose to start with Jarod instead. "Anything to report?"

"Nope. Been reading my cards, just like I agreed."

"Yes, I notice you've been diligent in checking off the app. Any progress?"

"I called some past customers. Got more work over the weekend than normal."

"Good. Anything—."

"That's all. Let's go on to Christy. I want to hear her news."

Mr. Griffin sighed. "Very well. Christy, how did the joint practice go?"

"Awesome. Coach Jan paired us up, one girl from our team with one girl from hers. They've got a Division I program, so everyone on her team is a top swimmer. They gave us some great advice and tons of encouragement. Coach Jan kept going from pair to pair, answering questions and giving feedback. At the end, she told us that our partner was going to be our 'big sister' for the year and we could call her whenever we needed advice, and she encouraged us to make time to swim with our big sisters whenever we could. She told us never to hesitate to call them, as the college swimmers would probably get more out of the relationship than we would. It was a nice thing to say, even if it's bogus."

"Don't be so quick to write it off. One of the reasons I love teaching is because of how much I learn."

"But we haven't taught you anything."

"First of all, you're wrong. Secondly, teaching this material forces me to go back to fundamental principles. Whenever I do that, I develop understandings that eluded me in the past or find that I've gotten lazy and let some things lag that I shouldn't have. There's no doubt that I raise my own level by teaching, and I think Coach Jan will find the same thing with her team."

Mr. Griffin sat on his desk. "I sense that you have more to share, Christy. You look both excited and disturbed."

"There's more. Coach Jan invited Dana, one of her past swimmers, to join the practice. Dana was a star on last year's team, and though she's still at the school getting her Masters, she can no longer swim because she's used up her athletic eligibility. At the end of the practice, Dana offered to be our coach."

"So you did it," Mr. Griffin said. "You found yourself a coach with time still left until your deadline. Did you like Dana?"

"She's great. We hit it off right away."

"So why do you look so uncomfortable?"

"There's more news. The Olympics coach kept his promise. He posted Kelvin's video and tagged all sorts of people. Based on the number of views, it seems like some of them shared it too. How many views do we have, Kelvin?"

"As of last period, 403."

Jarod stepped over to rustle my hair. "Nice going, dude."

"Yeah," Christy said, "but here's the problem. One of the women the coach tagged lives nearby. She was an alternate for the US Olympic team during the Atlanta Olympics, and later became a swim coach herself. She stopped coaching when she had kids, but the kids are a bit older now, and she was thinking about coaching again. She reached out to me over the weekend and said she'd help us out."

Mr. Griffin laughed. "As you progress, don't think your problems will go away. They'll just be replaced by higher quality problems. Two coaches may be uncomfortable, but it's far better than none."

Christy's hands twisted into each other. "So what do I do?"

"What do you *want* to do?" Mr. Griffin asked.

"Well, I've met Dana, but I haven't met the other woman. I suppose I should meet her."

"Sounds like a plan. You have your coaching notecard on you?"

"Right here, but it's pretty useless now."

"Useless? I doubt that. Read it off."

"It says:

> I intend to find an amazing coach for the girls' swim team by November 24.
> To accomplish this, I will do the following steps.
>
> 1. Research the top swimming coaches in the world
> 2. Make a list of 20 World Class Coaches to reach out to
> 3. Before each call, I will reconnect with my vision and get myself in a peak state of mind.
> 4. Call each coach, and be open to whatever help they offer to give.
> 5. Create a Team Video showing who we are and why we want to win so badly

"See, it's useless. I've done all of that."

"It's true that you've completed all of the steps listed, but that just means that they need updating. The goal and the deadline are as relevant as ever."

"So I just cross out the steps I've done?"

"Of course. The purpose of the card is to activate your mind toward your goal, to keep bringing you back to the work that lies ahead, and to motivate you to follow through. Have you found it motivating reading the steps you've already completed?"

"No, I was just doing it because you told me I had to or I'll fail math."

"You have to keep focusing on the *goal* and keep plugging away at the steps that will get you there. But you're looking at your steps in the rearview mirror. Let's make some changes. Are there any steps you feel you should keep at this point?"

"No. I've completed them all."

"Then cross them out. Or better yet, here's a new card. With all of those completed steps, you're out of room on that one."

"So I should copy over the top line of the old card?"

"Yes, the goal and the date are the same."

"What should I write for the steps?"

"You tell me."

Christy chewed the cap of her pen. "Well, the first step is that Jill and I should meet with Sue, she's the second coach. I suppose if we like her, we can ask her and Dana to each run a practice."

"What else?"

"Then we choose the one we like best, I guess."

"Can you think of any other options?"

"Not really." Christy turned to the rest of the class. "Any of you have ideas?"

"Maybe you don't need to choose," Darnell said. "Couldn't they both help you?"

"I think they'd get in each other's way, but it's possible. I see what you're saying. Why plan on choosing just one before I know for sure that they can't work together. After all, I can easily double my coaching budget."

"You can?" Jarod asked.

"Wake up Jarod, this is math class. Two times zero is still zero."

Mr. Griffin said, "Good use of your Mastermind Group, Christy. What will your new card read?"

Christy scribbled something down. "Now it says:

I intend to find an amazing coach for the girls' swim team by November 24.
To accomplish this, I will do the following steps.

1. Jill and I will interview all candidates
2. If the interview goes well, we'll ask the candidate to run a team practice
3. We will then decide on our top choice, while still being open to multiple coaches working together

---

"How are you going to do all of that in time?" I asked.

"What's that?"

I twisted around to look right at Christy. "You only have a few days until your deadline. Are you going to give Dana a real interview? If so, you need to do two interviews and two practices. When are you going to fit that all in?"

"I do want to give Dana a real interview. You're right, I might run out of time."

"Don't give up yet," Mr. Griffin said. "Deadlines have remarkable power to get us to think creatively. Can any of you come up with a way of saving Christy time?"

"Well, you already know that you like Dana enough to want her to run a practice," I said. "Couldn't you schedule her interview and her practice for the same day?"

"Good idea. That would save me a day."

"You still have no time to lose," Mr. Griffin said.

"You're right. Can I call them both now?"

"Go ahead."

Christy pulled out her cell phone and went over by the window at the back of the classroom.

"Guess this would be a good time to hit the john. Can I have a pass?" Jarod shot up, grabbed a pink note from Mr. Griffin and booked it out the door.

I grabbed my copy of Hamlet to study for my English exam, then saw Darnell take one furtive look at Christy and stepped up to Mr. Griffin's desk.

"Yes, Darnell?" Mr. Griffin asked.

Darnell fidgeted for a moment, then shot another glance toward the back of the classroom.

Mr. Griffin leaned in. "If you want to get it out before she gets off the phone, you'd better hurry."

Darnell's face hung low. "I'm embarrassed about my weight."

I quickly hid behind Shakespeare, but could still see Darnell through the corner of my eye. How could he be so open? I think I'd rather die than say that out loud.

"I know," Mr. Griffin said. "So was I at your age. You're ready to work on it?"

"Yes, but..." Darnell looked over his shoulder.

"Darnell, if I were to ask Christy, 'how do you think Darnell feels about his weight?' what do you think she'd say?"

Darnell's shoulders rose to meet his ears. "She'd say I was embarrassed."

"Sometimes what we consider our biggest secrets are stunningly obvious to the rest of the world."

Darnell's hands balled into fists. "Still..."

"It's possible for you to do this process alone. But I promise you—it's far more powerful when you open yourself up to the wisdom of your Mastermind Group."

"I know. I'm just not sure I can handle that."

"You strike me as a guy who wants to do it, but needs to be convinced. Is that right?"

Silence filled the air. Darnell drew a deep breath. "I suppose so."

"I can convince you, but it's going to hurt."

Darnell's head slowly rose so that his gaze met our teacher's. "I'm OK with that."

"Very well, then tell me, Darnell, if you're not able to address your weight now, when you're in a classroom full of people helping each other grow, when do you think you'll be able to take off the pounds?"

"Probably never."

"What about your attitude toward your weight? There are plenty of people who consider large bodies beautiful. If you're unable to ever lose the weight, do you at least think you can come to look at yourself as beautiful, despite your size?"

Darnell's back slumped. "No, Mr. Griffin."

"Close your eyes."

"Now? Here?" Darnell shot another glance towards Christy, who was still on the phone.

"Yes, now. Take a breath and relax your shoulders. There. Now, imagine you haven't changed your lifestyle at all. Picture yourself ten years from now, standing before a mirror. Can you see yourself?"

"Yes, but I don't want to."

"Do it anyway." There was a commanding tone to Mr. Griffin voice that I hadn't heard before. "Now, what do you look like?"

"I'm huge. My skin is all broken out. I keep dropping my eyes."

"Don't. Keep your eyes on the prize."

"The prize?"

"Yes, your efforts today lead to your rewards tomorrow. What you see in the mirror is the product of your choices today."

"Some prize."

"Tell me about the life of that man in the mirror. Are you confident?"

"No, I'm a mess. I can hardly look anyone in the eye."

"Do you have a good job?"

"No." Darnell's breathing grew short and shallow. "I'm working in some convenience store. With a boss who keeps pushing me around."

"Do you have a romantic relationship?"

"No, I'm alone." Darnell's face turned away.

"Back to the mirror, Darnell. Look right at him. This is your future. How's your health?"

"Awful. I can barely walk to work without getting short of breath."

"How do you feel now as you study the man in the mirror?"

"Nauseous. Gross. I want to squirm and run away."

"Good."

"How is this good?

"These feelings will give you the leverage you need to change. Now, look at that man in the mirror and tell him how you feel about him."

"You're disgusting!" Darnell's voice sounded blubbery, as though his lips were wet with tears.

Mr. Griffin reached over and dug his index finger into the soft flesh on the back of Darnell's shoulder. "Say it again."

"You're disgusting!"

"Again." Mr. Griffin pressed his finger into Darnell's shoulder each time.

"You're disgusting!"

"Remember this moment. It will be your greatest friend over the coming months." Mr. Griffin pulled his hand away. "Open your eyes. You did that exercise well. A little too well. Most teenagers have a harder time visualizing themselves in the future. At least, they have a harder time if they've never done it before. Do you spend a lot of time thinking about who you'll become?"

Darnell nodded and wiped his eyes with the back of his hand. "I'm scared of what will happen to me."

"And what do you do when you feel afraid?"

"I...eat."

"See a bit of a problem?"

Darnell's head tilted to the side, then popped straight again. "Yeah."

"What would happen if you put that fear behind you? What would happen if today you resolved to work hard until you had the body you wanted? If you were to decide right now to take the weight off and keep it off, what would that change?"

"Everything."

"Would it? Let's put it to the test. Close your eyes again. The same ten years have passed. You're staring in the mirror at a Darnell ten years older, but who's fit, who's got the body you dream of. What does this Darnell look like?"

Darnell's posture straightened—he actually seemed taller. "I look good. Really good."

"Tell me more. Are you thin?"

"Not exactly thin, but there's no fat on me. I'm muscular. An athlete."

"How's your confidence?"

"Super high. I'm smiling back at me."

"How's your health?"

"Amazing. I've got tons of energy."

"Job?"

"A great job, making a lot of money. Maybe in sales."

"Sales? So you're a people person?"

"Oh yeah."

"And a relationship?"

"Married to a beautiful woman."

"How do you feel now as you study the man in the mirror?"

"Awesome. My whole body is buzzing."

"Tell him how you feel about him."

"You rock!"

Mr. Griffin dug his finger into Darnell's chest. "Again."

"You rock!"

Again his finger dug in. "One more time."

"You rock!"

Mr. Griffin pressed his finger once more and removed it. "If this Darnell could speak to you and give you one piece of advice, what would it be?"

Darnell pounded his fist into his hand. "Don't be afraid."

"Open your eyes. You've told me your dream, and you've told me your nightmare. Are you ready to choose between the two?"

"Yes, Mr. Griffin."

"Are you willing to take your own advice and face your fears?"

"Yes."

"Can you get past your embarrassment so we can get to work?"

Jarod walked in the door. "I'm back. Don't all applaud at once, OK?"

Darnell's posture deflated.

"Can you get past your embarrassment?" Mr. Griffin repeated.

"I think so."

"That's not good enough. This can't come from me. Your homework tonight is to sit with these two visions for who you can become. Tomorrow I want you to tell me what you've decided."

Christy was now off the phone and chatting with Jarod.

"Christy, do you have an update for us?" Mr. Griffin asked.

"Good news with Dana. She's free today. She's going to run practice this afternoon, and she'll come early to meet with the captains beforehand."

"Great. And Sue?"

"I couldn't reach her."

* * *

Darnell entered the classroom with fire in his eyes. He shot Mr. Griffin a quick thumbs up and took his seat.

"We've got some exciting news today," Mr. Griffin said, "but first I want to get updates. Christy, how did the interview and practice go?"

"The interview went great. Dana's got so much enthusiasm. Jill and I both loved her."

"And the practice?"

"It was good. I don't think Dana's ever run one before. Things were a bit disorganized at first, but then she divided us into two teams and had us go through an entire swim meet. A big improvement over when we were running them ourselves."

"Any update on Sue?"

"She's going to come in and interview today."

"What about practice?"

"I didn't want to ask her yet, because then what would I do if the interview went poorly, say 'sorry, but we don't like you enough to ask you to run a practice?'"

Mr. Griffin laughed. "One of the reasons my first business failed was because I hated rejecting anyone. I'd hire people who weren't perfect fits, and resisted firing those who weren't working out. My breakthrough came when I realized that honest communication was not only better for me, it was better for them as well."

"Why was it better for them?"

"Because as long as they were wasting time with me, they weren't able to find a place where they could thrive. And when someone is not a good fit and isn't contributing value, they know it inside."

"So if we tell her we don't want her, she won't be bummed?"

"Of course she will—it hurts to be rejected. But that's only momentary pain. When we get too focused on avoiding short-term pain, we can cause far more in the long-term. After all, I'm sure Sue will have no problem finding another coaching job where she earns no salary."

Christy laughed. "Good point. We figured if the interview went well today, we'd invite her to run practice afterward, so we'd still make our deadline."

"Hopefully she'll be available. Jarod, how about you?"

"Doing OK, Mr. Griffin."

"Have you made any progress?"

"Some."

"Care to elaborate for the class?"

"Not really."

Mr. Griffin shook his head. "In that case, we move on to today's most exciting news." He clapped, then rubbed his hands together. "We have a new victim."

Without waiting for Mr. Griffin to call on him, Darnell stood and faced the class. "I'm sick of being fat. I don't want to go through life overweight and out of shape." He pulled a notecard out of his back pocket and read:

I intend to lose 70 pounds this year while building muscle and getting in shape.

Jarod clapped. Christy called out, "Go, Darnell!"

"Tell me, Darnell," Mr. Griffin said, "did that feel better or worse than you thought it would?"

"So much better. I thought people would laugh at me."

"No way, Darnell," Jarod said. "That took balls."

"See?" Mr. Griffin said. "Most people get inspired by someone who wants to face their challenges and grow."

"So you like my card so far?"

"I love the intention," Mr. Griffin said.

"But you don't like the card?"

"I'd like to tweak the language a bit."

"How's that?"

"If it's not too embarrassing, can you tell me how much you weigh now?"

"It is embarrassing." Darnell bit his lip. "I weighed myself this morning at 242 pounds."

"So if a couple of months from now you weigh yourself and find that you're 208 pounds, how far along will you be toward your goal?"

"That's easy, I'll take my starting weight of 242 and subtract 208, and I'll come up with, just a second, 34 pounds. I'll be almost halfway."

"Does anyone see a problem in what Darnell just did?"

The math was right. But Mr. Griffin said the other day that he was less concerned about the math than the psychology. Then it clicked.

"Darnell went back to his starting weight to figure out how much progress he'd made."

"Precisely Kelvin. Now, why is that a problem?"

"Is it because it reminds him that he used to weigh 242 pounds?"

"Exactly. For all I know, this could be the first day when Darnell weighed 242 pounds. Yesterday he might have been 241. Yet, if he creates his goal this way, each day he'll return to the fact that he used to weigh 242. Darnell, you want to leave that identity in the dust, yet if you keep focusing on it, you might reinforce it instead."

"So how would I write it better?" Darnell asked.

Mr. Griffin turned to me. "Kelvin, you figured out the first half of the puzzle. Can you get the rest?"

If going back to his old weight was reinforcing the wrong identity, what would strengthen the right one? "I suppose we could reverse it. Darnell, rather than say how much you want to lose, you could say what you want to weigh at the end. So 172 pounds."

"Or less," Darnell added.

"Excellent," Mr. Griffin said. "As we told Christy, we always want our goals centered on where we're going. We never want to look at them in the rearview mirror."

"Got it," Darnell said. "Now my card reads:

> I intend to weigh 172 pounds or less by the end of the school year while building muscle and getting in shape.

"Better Darnell, though I'd like to recommend one more change. Huge goals can be motivating, but also intimidating. Also, there is a tendency to delay starting if the end date is too far in the future. Let's shrink the change. You signed a contract agreeing to a 30-day commitment. How much do you intend to lose in the next month?"

"I can commit to 15 pounds."

"Excellent, so let's fix your card."

Darnell corrected his card, then said, "Now it reads:

> I intend to weigh 227 pounds or less by December 23

"Now, how will you get there?"

"I guess cut out the junk food and exercise more."

"Exercise more you say? Wonderful, stand up."

Darnell got to his feet.

"Good job, now sit down."

Darnell, clearly confused, sat down again.

"Congratulations. You just did more exercise."

All of us, including Darnell, laughed. "I see your point," he said, "I need to be more specific."

"Yes, you do. And cutting out the junk food might not be enough. You might need to cut the junk out of your normal food as well. Tell me, what did you have for breakfast yesterday?"

Darnell squirmed. "3 bowls of Frosted Flakes."

"Anything to drink?"

"2 glasses of orange juice."

"And that's just breakfast, I won't bother taking you through the rest of your day, but I believe you already see the problem."

Darnell nodded. "So what should I put down on my card?"

"You tell me. You know the procedures by now. You've got your Mastermind Group to help. What steps must you take to reach your goal?"

* * *

Classes were shortened the next day so families traveling for Thanksgiving could get an early start.

"We don't have a lot of time today, so let's dive right in," Mr. Griffin said. "Christy, how did the big interview with Sue go yesterday?"

"I'm not sure actually."

"What did you learn about her during the interview?"

"Nothing really. She asked most of the questions."

"Like what?"

"Like everything. She asked about the training methods our last coach used. She asked about the girls on the team and took notes on each one. She asked about the other teams in our conference. She would have kept going if we didn't have to break off for practice."

"Did you ask her to run the practice?"

"She refused. She said she'd need a couple of days to plan out her first practice. She stayed and watched though. Now and then she'd pull one of the girls aside and point something out. But that was it. She said the earliest she'd be willing to run a practice is Monday, after the holiday."

"Your deadline to hire a coach is today," Mr. Griffin said.

"I know. What should I do?"

"I can't answer that for you, Christy. You tell me."

"I definitely like Dana more. She ran a good practice, and all of the girls liked her. With Dana, I know we'd all work together to figure things out. That's not the way it would be with Sue. I don't think Sue cares about our opinions. I just wish I had until Monday so I could see her coach."

"You can't?" Mr. Griffin asked.

"You know I can't. You said yourself, today's the 24th."

"So?"

"So that's what's written on the notecard."

Mr. Griffin laughed. "Who's in charge, the notecard or you?"

"But you said yourself that we had to stick to the notecard deadlines."

"The notecards are a tool. They serve to activate your mind and keep you in line with your higher vision. When they work best, they can cause huge shifts in your life. Those very shifts can make what you originally wrote on the notecards outdated. That's why we change the steps so much, but we can also change the deadline or even the goal itself. The key is to know when a change will truly move you toward your higher vision, and when it's just a cop-out. Remember why you gave yourself this deadline?"

"It was the thought that if we went more than two weeks without coaching, we'd be sunk."

"Do you still feel that way?"

"No. The team's come a long way since then. We've already gotten some great coaching, and we're no longer a mess. At this point, I think we'd be silly not to give ourselves until Monday to make sure we get the best possible coach." Christy bent over her card, pen in hand.

Mr. Griffin turned to Darnell. "Now, how about you?"

"I weighed in this morning at a svelte 241 pounds." Though he had only lost one pound, Darnell beamed.

"How'd you do it?"

"I walked home from school yesterday rather than taking the bus, and I skipped dessert after dinner."

"Sounds like a strong start. How's your notecard coming along?"

"Good. It now reads:

I intend to weigh 227 pounds or less by December 23.
To accomplish this, I will do the following:

1. Cut out all soda, ice cream, and other junk foods, replacing
    them with healthier alternatives
2. Get at least half an hour of exercise per day

"Nice start. Jarod, any update for us?"

Jarod slouched in his chair in the back row, arms crossed. "Nope."

"Anything you'd like to run by your Mastermind Group?"

"I'm good."

"Very well. Have a great holiday, everyone."

* * *

On Monday, Darnell refused to make eye contact with any of us. Blood rose to his cheeks as he took his seat. A moment later, those same flabby cheeks glistened with the tracks of tears. He must have put on major pounds during Thanksgiving.

"Certain moments define a lifetime," Mr. Griffin said. "My gut tells me, Darnell, that you're in one of those moments right now."

Darnell's back trembled.

"How bad is it?" Mr. Griffin asked.

Darnell's voice quivered. "246."

"I'll remind you all," Mr. Griffin said, "our greatest clarity comes at times of extremes, at our greatest heights or our lowest lows."

Mr. Griffin stepped in front of Darnell's desk. "I could be nice right now—I could sympathize with you and help you feel less pain—but that wouldn't serve you. Use the pain you're feeling now to help you make the all-important decision that lies before you."

Mr. Griffin looked around the class. "For the rest of you, feel the emotion in the room. Tap into that to delve into your own places of brokenness." He sat back down at his desk. "There will be no speaking for the rest of class."

Mr. Griffin pulled out a worn journal and wrote. Darnell continued to sob into his arms.

Chapter Six

The Numbers Game

The next day, Darnell walked into class wearing a windbreaker over his clothes. The tears from the day before were gone, replaced by a quiet determination.

"Are you trying to sweat off the weight, Darnell?" Jarod asked. It was a testament to Darnell's composure that Jarod said anything—even he wouldn't have teased Darnell a day earlier.

"Something like that," Darnell said with a grin.

"Let's start with Christy," Mr. Griffin said. "Did you like Sue?"

"No. We all hated her. She bossed us around non-stop. She told us everything we were doing was wrong. I'm not just talking about our diving or swimming. She didn't even like the way we put on our goggles."

"So you hired Dana?" I asked.

"No, we hired Sue."

"You're kidding," Jarod said. "You hired someone you hated over someone you loved?"

"My notecard was clear." Christy took out the card and read:

I intend to captain the girls' swim team to victory in the State Championships on March 8th. To accomplish this, I will do the following:

1. Find an amazing coach

"If my goal were to have fun being team captain, I'd hire Dana. But my goal is to win, not be coddled. Sue was amazing. At the end of practice, I swam my fastest lap of the year."

"Was Dana disappointed?" Mr. Griffin asked.

"Actually, no. It's Dana's goal to be a top-notch coach someday, but I think she knows she's not there yet. When I told her how amazing Sue was, and that she was willing to take Dana on as an assistant coach, Dana jumped at it. So instead of hiring one coach, we hired two."

"I love how you keep saying you hired," Jarod said, "given that you're asking them to work *for free*."

"I know. It doesn't seem fair given that we did have money for a coach in this year's budget."

"So what's your next step?" Mr. Griffin asked.

"What do you mean?"

"You're out of steps on your card. You can already rip up the coaching card you made. And you can cross out step one on your championship card. What are you going to do now?"

Christy laughed. "I guess I was expecting Coach Sue to take charge. She knows a lot more about championship swimming than I do."

"Never delegate your vision. You've put yourself in a much better position by bringing on a top coach. Yet, the question remains, what can *you* still do to make your goal a reality?"

"I'm not sure."

"Well then, turn to your Mastermind Group."

"Do any of you have any ideas?"

Christy looked straight at me, yet Darnell answered first. "If everyone hates the coach, then even if she knows what she's doing, the team might fight her."

Christy nodded. "That's true. Dana, Jill, and I will have to work on keeping the team's spirits up."

Darnell added, "If you get the rest of the school behind your vision, that could also help get the girls on the team pumped up."

"I like that. You know, you have a lot of insights for a guy hiding behind a windbreaker."

"Oh, hiding, am I?" Darnell stood up and began unzipping his windbreaker.

"Yeah, Darnell!" Christy screamed. "Take it off!"

Darnell squirmed but kept pulling down the zipper. He turned his back to the class so he could pull off his jacket without showing us the front. "Introducing the newest fashion in weight loss," he said and spun around.

On the front of Darnell's shirt, three block numbers were written in tape: 2 4 5.

"Is that your weight?" Jarod asked.

"Yep."

"I thought you weighed 246?" Jarod said.

"I did. Yesterday."

"You're not afraid that people will make fun of you if you go around with your weight written on your chest?" Jarod asked.

"I'm counting on it. I've decided to use the embarrassment as motivation. But I have a sense that when the numbers start dropping below 200, even those who laugh at me now will start respecting what I've done."

"I respect you already, Darnell," Jarod said. "It takes a brave man to do that. I wouldn't have the guts."

"I've only got one shot at this. I've got to get it right."

"Why only one shot?" Jarod asked.

"I realized yesterday that I'm either going to come out of these 30 days believing that I'm stronger than my challenges, or that they're stronger than me."

Jarod didn't fire back a snappy comment. In fact, he didn't say anything at all. His face paled as if he'd been slapped.

"I love the attitude, Darnell," Mr. Griffin said. "Have you added this to your steps?"

"Yep, and that's not the only change. My card now reads:

I intend to weigh 227 pounds or less by December 23.
To accomplish this, I will do the following:

1. Cut out all soda, ice cream, and other junk foods, replacing them with healthier alternatives
2. Exercise at least one hour per day
3. Use the power of embarrassment by writing my current weight on my chest each day
4. Eat only when I'm truly hungry, and stop eating once I'm full

Mr. Griffin said, "I'm glad to see your steps getting stronger."

"They have to," Darnell said. "I've lost time and gained weight."

"Indeed," Mr. Griffin said. "My gut tells me that more changes await."

* * *

The next day Darnell wore a bright red sweatshirt with the number 244 taped on the front. Jarod entered after him and, rather than going to the back of the class, he took the seat behind me. Christy sat next to him, leaving all four of us clustered together in the front of the class.

When the bell rang, Mr. Griffin looked up from his notecards and grinned. "New seating arrangements I see."

Jarod just nodded back.

"Go on, Jarod," Mr. Griffin said. "Say what's on your mind. Take as long as you need."

"I want to be part of this class."

"Haven't you always been part of the class?" I asked.

"Not really. I sit in the back and do as little as possible. The only reason I even read my cards each day is so I won't flunk and lose the credit."

"What changed?" Mr. Griffin asked.

"At first, it was easy enough to blow off as just another dumb assignment from some teacher who thinks he knows what I need better than I do. But I still read the card. I knew these were my goals, not yours, and the steps made a lot of sense. And I felt like a shmuck each time I read the card, knowing I'm not going to follow through on most of it."

"That's why the repeated reading of the cards is so powerful," Mr. Griffin said. "As we read them, they program our unconscious mind. I can't read a card without acting on it for long. I need to either destroy it or follow through."

"Even while I was ignoring my card," Jarod said, "I watched Christy have all this success finding a coach. A couple of weeks ago, I thought she had no chance of winning the State Championship. Now I think she's got a real shot."

"Better than a shot." Christy punched his arm. "We're going to win this thing."

"You know, I believe you will."

"Really? I was expecting some snappy remark."

Jarod shook his head. "That's what I'm trying to say. I don't want to be the guy sitting in the back cutting jokes anymore."

"Did you get a lobotomy?" Christy said.

"Something like that. I owe it all to Darnell."

"Me?" Darnell's head spun. "What did I do?"

"You came in here a total mess on Monday. I'm sure you stuffed your face on Thanksgiving last year too, and probably never thought twice about it. But because of your stupid card, you came in here crying like a 246-pound baby.

Don't be offended, but that's what I thought. Seeing you was the final proof I needed that Mr. Griffin was just some jerk who came in here thinking he knew more than us but was just as clueless as most teachers.

"Then yesterday, Darnell, you displayed more guts than I've ever had in my entire life. I saw you take a look at your life and decide you want more. It made me look at my attitude and wonder why I wanted so little for myself."

"So what do you want from your life, Jarod?" Mr. Griffin asked.

"In the big picture, I guess I don't know yet. For now, I want to hit the goal on my card."

"Have you followed through with anything on your card?"

"A bit."

"Let's read it off and start from there."

Jarod read:

I intend to make $1000 between November 13 and December 13. To accomplish this, I will do the following:

1. Call all past customers who have not hired me in a while to see if they're interested in working with me again.
2. Print out a flyer and pass it around my neighborhood to get new customers. The flyer will not only say that I mow lawns, rake leaves, shovel snow, etc., it will also say who I am and why I want the money.
3. Keep my existing rate for customers willing to commit to one mow/lawn care per week, and raise my rate by $10 for one offs.
4. Call people with successful landscaping businesses until I reach someone willing to give me advice.

"Of these steps, which ones have you done?"

"Numbers 1 and 3. I've gotten quite a few more jobs than normal just by calling up past customers. And no one has given me a hard time on the rate change at all."

"So how much have you made since November 13?"

"$260."

"Look at that," Mr. Griffin said. "Even with weak follow through, you've already passed your old monthly average."

"That's one way to look at it. Another is that I've already blown over half my time, and made just over a quarter of my monthly goal."

"True. The clock is ticking on your goals. What's been the story with numbers 2 and 4?"

"Just lazy, I guess."

"Is laziness your issue?"

"Not when it comes to working. I have no problem doing lawns. But when it comes to those other things, I just can't seem to get started."

"Class, pay attention to the steps you don't find yourself getting around to. Jarod might tell himself it's laziness, but my guess is it's intimidation."

Jarod thought about this a moment. "Yeah, I do find them intimidating."

"Intimidation is like an arrow, pointing out precisely where you most need to grow to succeed."

"So I need to push myself to try harder on those?"

"No, try smarter. First, let's reword those two steps so it's impossible to wiggle out of them or push them off. How quickly can you get a flyer made?"

"I don't know. I've never made a flyer before."

"Do you have any experience with graphic design?"

"That's not my thing, Mr. Griffin."

"Is it any wonder you've made zero progress on this step? How many more lawns do you need to mow to become proficient at graphic design?"

Jarod laughed. "I see what you're saying. So now in addition to all the extra work, I need to take time to learn graphic design?"

"No. As you said, that's not your thing. Core to the Mastermind principle is that you can't be great at everything. Rather than chasing a multitude of skills that are beyond you, leverage the power of those who already excel in that area."

Jarod turned to me. "Kelvin, you did a great job with Christy's video. Do you know how to make flyers too? Could you help me out?"

"I can do that," I said. "Come by my place tonight, and we can get it done." Jarod knew where I lived; he used to come over all the time to play when we were kids. It had been almost ten years since he was over, though.

"Before you go to Kelvin's, I suggest you go to a print shop," Mr. Griffin added. "They can help you figure out your size options and give you the precise dimensions Kelvin will need to make the flyer."

"It's better if I do that," I said. "I'll need to know details such as the bleed. They may even have a template. All that can be confusing for anyone who doesn't know what they're doing."

"If you could do that for me, it would be amazing," Jarod said.

"OK, let's assign number 2 a specific date," Mr. Griffin said. "When will you have the flyer delivered?"

"Let's say it will be designed today, printed tomorrow, and passed out the next day," Jarod said. "So December 3."

"Great, add that to your step. Now, for number 4, I suggest adding the requirement of having one conversation per work day, voicemails not included. That way it's crystal clear. You'll know when you read your card what you have to do and whether or not you've accomplished it."

"I don't like it, but I'll do it. My card now reads:

I intend to make $1000 between November 13 and December 13. To accomplish this, I will do the following:

1. Call all past customers who have not hired me in a while to see if they're interested in working with me again.

2. Print out a flyer and pass it around my neighborhood to get new customers. The flyer will not only say that I mow lawns, rake leaves, shovel snow, etc., it will also say who I am and why I want the money. I will pass it out by December 3.

3. Keep my existing rate for customers willing to commit to one mow/lawn care per week, and raise my rate by $10 for one offs.

4. Call people with successful landscaping businesses until I reach someone willing to give me advice. I will have at least one conversation per work day.

"That's a big improvement." Mr. Griffin said. "Anything else you want to add?"

"Yeah. I appreciate you all being there for me." Jarod took the time to look at each one of us. "I'm going to try to be a better Mastermind partner. I want to be there for you as well."

* * *

After school, Darnell walked with me over to the printer's.

"Have people been teasing you like crazy?" I asked.

"A bit. Derek was picking on me at lunch. You know how he is. The more people he got laughing at his jokes, the bigger jerk he became. But then Jarod heard, and he came over."

I stopped in my tracks. "Don't tell me he told Derek off?"

"No, he wouldn't. They're buds. But you know how it is with those guys. All Jarod had to do was tell me loud enough for everyone to hear how impressed he was with what I was doing and how he's totally behind me. After that, Derek left me alone."

I knew what Darnell meant. Derek wasn't about to tease Jarod, so that left him little choice but to let Darnell be.

"You know," Darnell said, "I don't think it's going to be anywhere near as bad as I feared. Even before Jarod came over, Derek wasn't as brutal as usual. It's almost like they tease you about the things you're trying to hide, but when you just come right out and give them the ammo, they don't know how to handle it."

"Jarod's right, you've got guts."

"Maybe. That part hasn't been so bad, but the hunger is getting to me."

"What have you been doing for exercise?"

"Mainly just walking to and from school. I know I ought to do more, but between homework, dinner, and watching a bit of TV, I haven't found the time."

We reached the printer's. "Are you coming in?"

"No, I'll head on home. See you later."

When I got home, Mom was washing dishes. "How was school?" she asked.

"Fine."

"You still haven't told me about your math teacher…"

"Nothing much to tell." I picked an apple from the fruit bowl on the counter and walked over to wash it. "He's not exactly teaching us math."

Mom made room for me at the sink. "So what is he teaching you?"

I bit into my apple on my way out of the kitchen and mumbled, "Nothing really."

I went to my room, shut the door, and pulled out my notecard. I called it version 1.12, yet even this one was getting worn from edits. I read it off, as I'd been doing at least ten times per day, but it still didn't feel right. I had a feeling it would only be a day or two until I replaced it with version 1.13.

If I couldn't get my own goal in order, at least I could help others with theirs. I fired up my mac and loaded up the templates from the printer into Photoshop. I didn't bother trying to manipulate them. I'd wait until Jarod came to go over the pricing options and choose the right size.

Instead, I looked up a couple of email addresses and sent off a message with links to the video I'd made for the girls' swim team. Then I went onto

Craigslist to do a bit of research.

Jarod arrived early in the evening, his brow dotted with flecks of grass. He looked around my room, and old memories flashed in his eyes. "Thanks for this." He extended a hand for a shake.

"Anytime."

Before getting to work on his flyer, I told him about my other plan, and he quickly agreed to help. It took us just two quick phone calls to arrange everything. Once that was done, I opened Photoshop, and the two of us got to work.

* * *

"Jarod," Mr. Griffin asked, "how did it go with the graphics yesterday?"

"Awesome. Kelvin's the man." Jarod patted my shoulder. "He designed a killer flyer and emailed it to the print shop last night, so I can pick up a stack on my way home. I'll pass them out tonight."

"Maybe you could also email the flyer to your current customers," Christy added.

"Yeah," Darnell joined in, "and post it on social media, and ask your friends to share it."

"What do you think of that, Jarod?" Mr. Griffin asked.

"I'm diggin' it." Jarod pulled out his notecard. "I'll add that now. I could get all of that done by tomorrow."

"Make any phone calls yesterday?" Mr. Griffin asked.

"I actually got the biggest landscaping guy in town on the phone. He said flatly that he wasn't interested in strengthening his competition. So no luck there."

"I'm not so sure," Mr. Griffin said.

"Really? How?"

"There's a critical point that I want you all to grasp. Don't think life happens *to* you. The truth is, life happens *for* you. Every experience you have is packed with lessons—you just need to tune in to receive them. Like a radio. Radio waves are around you at all times, but until you adjust to the right frequency, you won't hear anything."

"So what do you think I got from the call?" Jarod asked.

"You tell me. What are three lessons you can take away from that call?"

"I don't know. Maybe that I was pushing off making calls because it's not my thing, but once I did it, it wasn't so bad."

"That's one. What else?"

"I was afraid that I'd get his secretary and would get the runaround, but it turned out that after hours he answered his own phone."

"That's two. One more."

Jarod's brow creased. Suddenly, a big smile drew across his face. "The largest landscaping guy in town considers me competition."

"That's right. In your mind, you're just some kid with a lawnmower. But I bet this guy started out the same way, and he knows how powerful one kid with determination can become. Yesterday at this time he probably didn't know who you were, but after one phone call, he sees you coming for him. Any other takeaways from the call?"

"I think I'll start calling the big landscapers from other towns. They won't feel as threatened by me, so that won't keep them from helping."

"Wonderful. That's a fourth thing you've learned. Remember, the activated mind never lacks opportunities for improvement. What a minute ago was a worthless call you've now turned into life lessons you'll never forget."

Mr. Griffin turned towards Darnell. "Any update?"

Darnell wore a blue sweatshirt with the number 243 on the front in black tape. "I can get an extra hour a day of exercise in. Thanks to Kelvin and Jarod."

"Oh? Kelvin strikes again?" Mr. Griffin turned toward me. "What did you do this time?"

"I found someone getting rid of an old treadmill on Craigslist. They just wanted someone to come pick it up. Since Jarod was coming over anyway, the three of us were able to haul it in the back of Jarod's pickup."

"Then we set it up in my living room," Darnell said. "That way, I can get exercise even while watching TV."

"Good thinking," Mr. Griffin said. "How about you, Kelvin, have you thought any more about what you'd like to work on in this class?"

I dropped my eyes. "No. Not yet."

Mr. Griffin studied me for an uncomfortably long moment. "Very well," he finally said, though I could tell he didn't believe me. "You'll let us know when you're ready. Now Darnell, make sure you add the treadmill to your card. Then read what you have to your Mastermind Group and be ready for feedback."

* * *

Darnell's family spent most fall weekends watching football together. The couple of times I'd joined them, there'd been no lack of nachos, soda, pizza, and a half dozen other treats at these games. While it wasn't quite as bad as Thanksgiving, I nonetheless wondered how far back the weekend would set him.

Darnell came into class on Monday with the number 242 on his chest. While only one pound lower than the 243 he'd worn on both Thursday and Friday, it was still progress and meant he hadn't regressed during the weekend. Still, it was already December 6, almost two weeks since he'd started, and he was only at his starting weight.

"Christy," Mr. Griffin said, "how is the team coming together?"

"Amazing. Everyone's times are up. We won our first meet of the season yesterday. A reporter from the town paper came and covered it, and she wants to interview Jill and myself this afternoon. Apparently, someone sent the paper's editors the video, and they think there's a story there."

Christy shot me a smile. Was that just because of the success of the video, or did she suspect that I was the one who sent it to the paper's editors?

"Are the girls warming to the coach at all?"

"They don't like her, but they respect her and listen to her. Winning the meet certainly helped. And Dana, Jill, and I have been working to bolster team spirit. We're coming together."

"Wonderful. Jarod, any success with the flyer?"

"Four new clients. I've got a job booked every day this week. Plus, I worked my butt off over the weekend. I'm already over $500 for the month."

"Reach any more landscapers?"

"One. He was short and to the point. He said, 'just keep plugging away, kid. You'll get there.'"

Mr. Griffin nodded, then began pacing back and forth in front of the class. "There's something going on in this room that's bothering me."

"What's that, Mr. Griffin?" Darnell asked.

"I'll tell you in a minute. First, do you have an update for us, Darnell?"

"I walked on my treadmill for over four hours yesterday while watching football. I'm not getting winded as fast as I used to."

"Good," Mr. Griffin said, though I could tell from his pacing that he wasn't all that engaged with what Darnell said.

Finally, I asked, "What's bothering you, Mr. Griffin?"

"It's you, Kelvin."

"Me? What did I do?"

"Everything. You made a video for Christy that helped her land a fabulous coach. You made a flyer for Jarod that got him four new customers in just a few days. You got Darnell a treadmill so he can exercise while watching TV. When's it going to end?"

"You say it like these are bad things."

"Bad? No, none of these are bad. But I keep wondering: what is your vision? What is it you want? When are you going to give the rest of the class a chance to help you like you're helping them?"

Mr. Griffin wasn't going to let me hide much longer, but I could still push it "I haven't been able to think of anything yet."

"No? Are you sure?"

"Of course I'm sure. Why wouldn't I tell the class if I knew what I needed?" My gut told me Mr. Griffin knew exactly what I wanted. Didn't he realize that I just couldn't just come out and say it?

"Very well, then. If you truly don't know, I have an assignment for you. Your homework is to ask yourself what need you fill when doing so much for others. I don't mean things like Christy needing a video person or Jarod needing a graphic designer. I mean, what need within yourself are you filling. Answer that, and I think you'll find your vision."

Chapter Seven

A False Identity

"At this pace, I expect I'll end up with around $800," Jarod reported that Thursday.

The week had passed in a blur. I was caught up on Mr. Griffin's question about what I hoped to gain from helping so much. For the past three days, I hardly participated in class and hadn't done anything to help anyone after school. As far as I could tell, no one had noticed.

"That's great," Christy said.

"Is it?" Mr. Griffin asked.

"For 30 days?" Jarod asked. "Absolutely. A month ago I only did $250."

"What does your card say?"

"It says $1000. But we all know I was only going half-assed the first couple of weeks, so $800 is pretty good."

"Pretty good?" Mr. Griffin asked. "Is that the expectation you have for yourself?"

"Didn't you once say that what we're going for is growth and we don't always hit our goals?" Jarod said.

Mr. Griffin shook his head. "If next Tuesday, after your deadline has passed, you tell me that you hit 98% of your goal, I'd tell you to celebrate your growth, and not beat yourself up over the other 2%. But there are still five days to go until your deadline. This is not the time to pat yourself on the back. It's time to reevaluate your strategy and double your efforts."

Jarod tensed up, and his mouth opened for some snappy reply, but then his body relaxed, and he merely said, "What more can I do?"

"You tell me."

"I'm already booked today, tomorrow, Saturday morning, and Monday afternoon."

"You can't fit any more time in on the weekend?"

"I could work a few more hours on Saturday if I had enough work."

"Can you earn $200 in a few hours?"

"No."

"Then it's not enough. What about Sunday?"

"I promised my girlfriend I'd spend the day with her."

"You promised yourself you'd hit $1000 by the end of the month. Perhaps she can help you and then you'd fulfill both promises at once."

Christy snickered at the thought.

"She wouldn't go for that," Jarod said.

"Then you have a problem of misalignment," Mr. Griffin said.

"Misalignment?"

"Your goals and your girlfriend's goals are different. She's rightfully going to put pressure on you to fulfill your obligation to her, and it could come at the expense of fulfilling your obligation to yourself."

"So what do I do?"

"Get your goals aligned," Mr. Griffin said.

"How?"

"Tell me about your girlfriend. Does she genuinely care about you?"

Christy broke in, "It's almost *disgusting* how much she worships him."

Before Jarod could respond, Mr. Griffin said, "She wants you to be happy?"

"Yes."

"She wants you to be successful?"

"Sure."

"And you've talked to her about your goal for yourself this month and how important it is to you to reach it?"

Jarod fidgeted with his notebook. "It never actually came up."

Mr. Griffin held up his index finger. "Step one of alignment is to tell her about your goals. You might be surprised at how supportive she becomes just knowing what your goals are."

"She still won't be happy about me canceling on her."

Mr. Griffin held up a second finger. "Step two: what can you do to make sure she will be happier with you hitting your goal than with you taking her out on Sunday?"

"She doesn't like being canceled on."

"No one does. Is there anything she has her heart set on?"

"She did drop a hint about Cirque Du Soleil coming next month. She's dying to go, but the tickets cost $100 each."

"$100 is a small price to pay for alignment."

"I'm not going to send her alone, so it's not $100, it's $200. And even if she lets me work all day Sunday, there's no guarantee I'll hit $1000 for the month."

Mr. Griffin grinned. "Don't promise her the tickets in exchange for allowing you to cancel on Sunday. Rather, tell her about your goal to hit $1000 this month, and tell her that if you hit that goal, the two of you will celebrate by going to Cirque du Soleil. If she cares enough about the tickets, she might even help you hit the goal. And she'll do it joyfully, without giving you a hard time for canceling, because you'll be fully aligned."

"That might handle one problem," Jarod said, "but even if I had all of Sunday to work, I don't have enough jobs to make another $200. I've already hit up all of my normal customers."

"Use your Mastermind Group."

Jarod turned to the three of us. "You guys have any ideas?"

His eyes mainly fell on me. Ideas kept flickering in my head, and I knew that if I put my mind to it, I could probably help him brainstorm something that would work. Yet, as I'd done all week, I bowed out. "I've already given you my best ideas."

"What if you offer half off for new customers?" Darnell said.

Jarod shook his head. "Then I'd have to mow an extra $400 worth of lawns to get the missing $200. Even if I could line up that many jobs, I wouldn't have the time to do it."

"Then flip the offer," Christy said. "Buy one now, get one next month free."

"That's even worse, it's giving everyone two mows at half price."

"Yes, but this way you make all the money now and do the free work later. All of it still counts towards your goal."

"Even if I did want to do that, how would I get that many jobs?"

"How about another flyer?" Christy said. "You could put it in mailboxes around town, stipulating that they need to have their first mow this weekend to qualify."

"Let me get this straight," Jarod said. "I'd pay $50 to get a new flyer printed up. I'm already working all afternoon today and tomorrow, so I'd have to pass it around at night. To get an additional $200 worth of jobs, I'd have to promise $200 of free work next month. And to top it off, I don't get to put a dollar of that extra $200 in my pocket because I have to blow it on tickets to Cirque du Soleil. So I wind up working my butt off only to have $50 less in my pocket at the end of the day. I'm far better off doing nothing and hitting $800 for the month."

"As your math teacher," Mr. Griffin said, "let me say that your numbers are spot on."

"So you agree I shouldn't do it?"

"Absolutely not. Not all problems involving numbers are math problems."

"What's that supposed to mean?"

"Think, Jarod. What will you miss if you do it your way?"

"I'll miss hitting my goal. But in this case, missing the goal will be better than hitting it."

"I'd agree with you if your goal was to add as much money as possible to your college fund. Pull out your notecard."

Jarod pulled out his card.

"Read it. What's the goal?"

"I intend to mow $1000 worth of lawns between November 13 and December 13."

"Does the card say anything about how much money you intend to add to your college fund?"

"No." Jarod reached into his backpack and pulled out an eraser.

"What are you doing?"

"Changing the goal to add that bit about my college fund."

"Don't go changing it now."

"But it will be better for me like this."

Mr. Griffin shook his head. "No way."

"I told you from the beginning that this is the reason I wanted to get the money to begin with."

"You may have told me that, but you didn't put it on your card."

"So what? We've all made tons of changes to our cards."

"Not all changes are the same. Anything can change when it supports the goal. Steps are the most flexible, they should be getting stronger as you dive into them. Dates change when they must, such as Christy moving her deadline to give Sue time to run a practice."

"So goals can never change?"

"Even a goal can change when you decide it's no longer something you want. In this case, the goal is earning more money, which is something you want."

"The way I'd reword the goal, making it about money saved rather than money earned is a better reflection of what I really want."

"Then it makes perfect sense to change the wording. On Tuesday."

"But my 30 days end on Monday."

"Precisely. You gave yourself a goal for this month. Hit that goal. On Tuesday, when you write a new card, you'll take all you've learned this month and use it to make next month's goals even better."

"Why not just change it now?"

"Because every goal hit builds momentum, and every goal missed kills it."

"So I should finish the goal I wrote, even if it's not good for me?"

"Hitting your goal will be the best thing possible for you. It might mean working harder and having $50 less in your college fund, but think of all it will bring you. The flyer can potentially bring you a slew of new clients. True, you'll owe them a free mowing next month, but some of them might come back again and again afterward. You'll get to take your girlfriend to Cirque du Soleil, which aside from being a fantastic show, will be a well-deserved celebration for hitting your goal, will get the two of you in deeper alignment, and might even raise your status in her eyes."

"Like we need that." Christy rolled her eyes.

"But the main reason I don't want you to change your goal is selfish. If you change your goal, it will hurt my ability to hit mine."

"What's your goal?"

"The same it's been from the start. To make all of you into the successful, capable people you have the potential to be."

"What does my goal have to do with that?"

"It's simple. If you work your butt off to hit your $1000 goal by Monday, you'll know that you're capable of setting a goal and hitting it. The next time you write a card, will you word it better or worse?"

"Better, I expect."

"Will you set it higher or lower?"

"Higher of course."

"Right, because you'll know you're someone who sees goals through to the end. This is how you build momentum in life."

Mr. Griffin bent over and looked Jarod in the eyes. "Your goal is so close. One more push and you can hit it. Give up on it now and how much confidence will you have next time you set a goal that you'll see it through to the end?"

Jarod bit his lip. "Not much, I guess."

"And how likely are you to skip goal setting altogether?"

"I probably wouldn't bother."

"Exactly. I already know what you can do. In these next five days, you'll prove it to yourself. Work your butt off if you have to. Don't think about the $50 less you'll have in your college fund, think about the strength you'll build by seeing your goal through to the end. And when you go to Cirque du Soleil, enjoy every minute of it knowing that you've earned it."

* * *

Despite abstaining to volunteer my help, when Jarod called that evening, I begrudgingly agreed to help him with his new flyer.

I used the template from the previous one and switched out some of the text and an image. The entire thing only took me 20 minutes, but Jarod still acted like I'd pulled off a miracle.

Jarod's mom was away for the weekend, so he held a party at his house. Of course, I still wasn't invited. The funny thing is, if I needed something, I bet he'd be happy to help, just like he was happy to help bring Darnell's treadmill in his pickup. Yet, to include me in his party, no way. There were social boundaries he wouldn't cross.

So I sat home alone on yet another Friday night. Well, technically I was babysitting, but who was I kidding? Megan was more than capable of looking after herself, and I knew she'd sit in the den watching TV all night. Darnell had called to ask if I wanted to hang out, but I passed. At least I'd get $20 for watching Megan.

I ordered us a pizza when our folks went out and told her when it was time to go to sleep. Otherwise, I sat in my room and worked on my notecard. I'd lost count of the number of versions I'd made. I still couldn't figure out all of the steps I'd need to go through, but I knew the goal.

I couldn't speak to the class about it. No way. But I was sick of spending Friday nights on my own. I made my decision. I'd bring it up to Mr. Griffin on Monday.

* * *

Jarod didn't show up for class Monday morning.

Darnell wore the number 237 on his chest. He had ten days to go but had only achieved a third of his goal. That meant he had to lose a pound a day.

An article had come out in the local paper about the girls' swim team. Christy went on and on about the enthusiasm on the team. But the article had other impacts as well. Several girls had approached her about trying out for the team, even though it was mid-season, and their roster was set. And a man whose son had also been killed by a drunk driver committed $4000 to compensate the coaches.

I could barely pay attention. I was too focused on my impending conversation with Mr. Griffin.

When the bell finally rang, I stayed in my seat pretending to write something in my notebook. I waited until Christy and Darnell left class, then approached Mr. Griffin's desk. "Is there a time I can come talk to you? Alone?"

Something in his eyes made me suspect he'd been waiting for the question. "I'll wait for you here after school."

I returned right after the final bell rang.

"You can shut the door," he said. "I imagine you'll want to keep this private."

As the door clicked shut, the cross-breeze in the room died. Part of me wanted to pull the door open again and run. Instead, I faced Mr. Griffin. "How much do you know?"

"I don't know anything." Mr. Griffin sat back in his chair. As a businessman only teaching part-time, I feared he might be in a hurry to rush out at the end of the day. Yet, he fixed me with a sympathetic glance that told me he'd wait as long as I needed. "All I have are guesses."

"You've been guessing right all along. There is something I've wanted." I pulled the latest version of my dog-eared notecard from my pocket. I unfolded it, sucked in a full breath, and read:

I intend to take Monica Grey out on a date for New Year's Eve

No change registered on Mr. Griffin face, which told me he'd suspected it was something like this. "Did you write down any steps?"

"Many. I crossed them all out. I don't believe any will work."

"You've been working hard on this?"

I nodded. "I've done over twenty cards. It used to say Homecoming, but that came and went. Now even New Years is getting too soon. I've been thinking of changing it to Senior Prom."

"This card is different from all the others." Mr. Griffin rubbed his eyes. "Notecards are powerful tools for directing your will. But this card is about directing the will of another. It's possible, but you must tread carefully."

Was he going to help me or not?

"What do you think it would take for her to go out with you?"

I took another deep breath. At least we were moving forward. "I guess she'd have to see beneath my shyness. See the *real me*."

"The real you? I see. Tell me about this Monica."

"She's beautiful. I've had a crush on her for years."

"Is she popular?"

"Very."

"What are three things the two of you have in common?"

I bit my thumbnail.

"Can you think of even one?"

I shook my head.

"Have you ever spoken to her?"

"A bit. We were in chemistry together last year. A couple of times we were assigned to be lab partners."

"Has she ever shown the least bit of interest in you?"

My eyes burned. "No."

"Do you find it ironic that you want her to see beneath your exterior, but all you've seen is hers?"

I shrugged.

Mr. Griffin got to his feet. "What if this Saturday night she and some friends got together, and they invited you to join. Would you go?"

"Of course."

"They drive out to the lookout, and someone pulls out a bottle of whiskey. Monica pours two glasses, keeping one for herself, and extending one to you. Do you take it?"

"Probably."

"A couple of hours later, there are three empty bottles. Someone mentions getting home before curfew, so you all pile into the car. Do you go?"

"I don't know, Mr. Griffin."

"That's a scary thought, Kelvin."

It was scary.

"Kelvin, look at me. I want to make sure you hear what I'm about to say."

I slowly lifted my head and met his gaze. "You don't have a vision for yourself. You have a vision for other people."

A ball grew in my throat. Mr. Griffin was right, but I couldn't say so.

"I was a geeky kid in school myself." He ran his fingers through his hair. "I didn't have many friends. I could have—there were a few other geeky kids, and we probably would have had fun together."

"Why didn't you?" Somehow it was easier to look him in the eye now that we were speaking about him, not me.

"I wanted to fit in with the cool kids, and I knew I'd kill any chance of that if I hung out with the geeks. So I shunned them. I spent several years mostly alone, rejecting the kids who could have been my friends simply because everyone else also rejected them. Of course, they also wanted to be popular, so they didn't want to be seen with me any more than I wanted to be seen with them."

My mind went to Darnell. I was so upset that Jarod didn't invite me to join him and his friends on Friday night that I gave little thought to the fact that I'd blown off the one guy who *had* invited me. "So all of you were alone?"

"No. I was one of the lucky ones. Two of the other geeky kids didn't fare so well."

"What happened to them?"

"One of them got his wish. He decided he'd do whatever it took to become popular. He started off doing drugs. Before long he was selling them."

"And the other one?"

"Took his own life."

My stomach clenched.

"The real shame of it was that both of them could have had entirely different futures waiting just around the corner."

"What do you mean?"

"The guy who turned to drugs was brilliant. He easily could have gone to MIT or Cal Tech with others like him. This was right around the time when being a geek was starting to become cool, when geeks were changing the world. MIT was where I first found a circle of close friends, and it might have been the same for him."

"Might?"

"Yes, he might have found friends there. There's no question people would have liked him. The bigger question was, would he have allowed himself to be liked?"

"Why wouldn't he?"

"There's a reason we call middle and high school the formative years. If we're not careful, we can cement destructive beliefs about ourselves. The stories we tell ourselves can be so powerful that even when our circumstances change, we may fail to adapt."

"So if he believed he was unlikeable…"

"Then he might not have let others in, even when around others who wanted to be his friend."

"What happened to him?"

"His grades plummeted. He didn't care about learning anymore. Last I heard, he was recently out of prison and working as a janitor somewhere."

"And the guy who killed himself?"

"He was an artist. Horribly picked on as a kid. I think he would have had an even easier time finding a community of friends in places like Greenwich Village or San Francisco."

"What does this all mean for me?"

"There are no shortcuts, Kelvin. Everything you want is attainable, but it comes from building yourself, not swaying others. Right now, I fear you just want to become the person you think others want you to be."

Mr. Griffin had first called me out for helping others in class. Was he saying I should stop that? "But I liked it when I was helping the others with their cards."

"Then by all means, do it. Just make sure you're doing it out of your love for helping, not out of some ulterior motive."

"What do you think my motive is?"

"I think you want them to like you. I think you're disappointed that they haven't responded with the friendship you want. Let me guess: they appreciate your help, but don't invite you to join them and their friends."

"Except for Darnell. He'd like to be better friends. Of course, he's no more popular than I am."

"At this rate, he will be. Darnell's decided what he wants, and he's going for it with everything he's got. He may be getting teased now, but he's going to win the respect of a ton of people. I can't say the same for you. You're too busy looking over your shoulder to see how others react to everything you do."

"So what do I do now?"

"It's time you get the love of the one person who truly matters."

"Who's that?"

Mr. Griffin lifted his brow.

"Oh, right." I squirmed. "But how do I do that?"

"First step, tear up that notecard. We both know you're not going to win Miss Monica's heart, and even if you did, you wouldn't find the satisfaction you expect."

I looked down at the card only to see that I'd rolled it tight like a cigarette. I crumpled it and threw it in the trash. It was strange, after all of the energy I'd put into this goal, how much relief I felt with the notecard gone.

Mr. Griffin handed me a blank card. "You're going to write a new kind of notecard."

"What goes on it?"

"All of the attributes you want to see in yourself."

"With a 30-day deadline, like the others?"

"No. This card is not future-oriented. It's not about who you intend to become in a month. This is an Identity Card. It's about who you are now."

I swallowed hard. "But I don't like who I am now."

"That's because you've put other people in the driver's seat."

"I still don't get it."

"If you passed a drunk bum on the street and he called you dumb, how would you feel?"

"I wouldn't feel much of anything. I'd ignore him."

"You're going to MIT, correct?"

"Yeah, I got in early."

"Now, what if the dean of MIT called you dumb?"

My chest constricted. "That would suck."

"Why wouldn't you blow him off like you did the bum?"

"Cause the bum is...a bum. The dean of MIT deals with the smartest people in the world."

"But who decides that one is worth listening to and the other isn't?"

"Me, I guess."

"So who is making you feel bad?"

"The dean is."

"Not so fast now, you could have ignored the dean as you ignored the bum. Instead, you took the dean's words and beat yourself with them."

Something clicked. "When people teased Darnell in the past, it made him feel horrible. Now he's using their words to motivate him to exercise and eat better."

"You've got it!" Mr. Griffin pointed his pen at me. "Their words can't hurt Darnell. Only he has the power to do that."

"So only I have the power to like myself?"

"Exactly. Let's say Darnell asks you to hang out. How do you feel?"

"Okay, I guess. Nothing special."

"And who's the most popular kid in school?"

"Derek Andrews."

"If he invited you over, how would you feel?"

"Really good."

"Why?"

"Cause it would mean he's accepting me, that he thinks I'm cool."

Mr. Griffin leaned further back. "And what would that mean about you?"

"That I'm all right."

"And who decides that?"

"Right...I do." I rubbed my forehead. "So it's not the school's opinion that counts, it's mine?"

"Precisely. The Identity Card will help you shape your opinions of yourself and heed those opinions. It's based on what *you* think is important and what *you* value." Mr. Griffin pulled out a notecard. "Give me one trait you want to build in yourself."

"Popularity," I said, cringing.

"That's not a trait in you, it's in other people. What do you want to develop in yourself?"

"I dunno. I just don't want to be a loser anymore."

"Well, what traits do you admire in other people? Take Derek. What do you admire about him?"

"That he's popular. And all the girls think he's hot."

"Those are not traits in him, they're just the opinions of others. What quality of Derek's do you appreciate?"

"Oh." I pinched my lips. "Nothing really. He's a jerk."

"Can you think of someone who has qualities you *do* admire?"

"The director of my hacker camp, Jimmy."

Mr. Griffin smiled for the first time that afternoon. "What about him?"

"He's generous with his time. Last month, he spent an hour on the phone with me, helping me on a huge assignment for AP Computer Science. And he seemed happy to do it."

"Beautiful. That will be the first trait on your card. Write down, 'I am generous.'"

"Me?"

"Yes, you." Mr. Griffin poked his finger into my chest. "If you're admiring the quality in another, it's because that quality lives in you. And haven't you been generous with your Mastermind Group?"

"A bit. But what about all of those ulterior motives you mentioned when I helped the others?"

"Don't set the bar so high that you'll never be able to climb over it. You don't have to have 100% pure motives for your actions to be generous. Go ahead, write down, 'I am generous.' What else do you admire about Jimmy?"

"He's caring. He checks up on me during the year, even though it's totally not his job."

"Great. Write down, 'I am caring.'" Mr. Griffin tapped on the card. "And don't be so hesitant. No one who doesn't care about others would ever come up with that goal. Write it down. What else?"

"He's funny."

"Put it down. Put them all down. Anything you admire, you already have within you. And don't stop with Jimmy. Think of anyone you respect, even if only a little. Think of what you like about them—these are qualities you're going to learn to see in yourself."

"What about the steps?"

"We'll get to the steps later. Your homework for tonight is just to write the traits. Got it?"

"I think so."

Mr. Griffin grabbed his laptop and stepped to the door. "Excellent. Then I'll see you tomorrow."

* * *

Jarod was back in school on Tuesday with a bounce in his step.

"Where were you yesterday, Jarod?" Mr. Griffin asked.

"Working from sunrise till sunset."

"From the look on your face, I can tell you hit your goal."

"$1025. Sorry I had to miss school to finish."

"Not at all. To paraphrase Mark Twain, 'you should never let schooling interfere with your education.'"

"Not a chance of that," Jarod said.

"Yes, you've made it quite clear in the past that you were usually happiest when doing the least amount that school requires. That brings you to a crossroad." Mr. Griffin unlocked the drawer of his desk and pulled out a paper. "Here's your signed contract. You've completed your 30-day commitment."

Jarod took the contract and tore it down the middle. "I'm sticking with the process. I don't need this to motivate me anymore."

"So glad to hear it. Have you thought about what you want on your next card?"

"I'm bumping up my goal to $1500."

"Excellent. Glad to hear you're making progress. I do want to hear more about you hitting your goal this weekend, but there's another piece of business we need to get to today. We have our last victim."

"Kelvin, you finally jumping in?" Christy said.

"I am."

"About time. So what's your big goal?"

I hesitated, then looked at Mr. Griffin. "Go on," he said.

I pulled out my card and read:

I am generous, caring, funny, smart, loving, loyal, creative, imaginative, dependable

---

I stopped reading and put down my card. A confused silence filled the room.

"Don't forget humble," Jarod said.

"Shut up, Jarod," Christy said. "Kelvin, what's your goal?"

I searched Mr. Griffin's eyes for help, but he just gestured for me to answer.

Sitting there with everyone watching me, I wasn't sure I understood the goal either. I recalled what Mr. Griffin had told me the day before, but I still felt foolish. "To get to like myself." I couldn't hold back and added, "And get others to like me."

Mr. Griffin sighed at my comment. That might not have been his goal, but it was still one of mine. Then, before he could respond, Jarod said, "All of us already like you."

"Really?" Hot anger rose to my cheeks. "Then why didn't you invite me to your party last Friday?"

Jarod laughed. "That's why you're all bent out of shape? Kelvin, the last time I sent out invitations for a party was for my tenth birthday, and you were there if you'll recall. I just told a couple of guys that my mom was going away for the weekend, and before I knew it, there were forty people at my house on Friday night. Not one of them was invited. They all just heard something was going on and came over."

"Oh right, so I was welcome to just come on by?"

"You were as welcome as anyone else."

"And I suppose if I'd come, I'd have fit right in?"

"No, you probably would have squeezed yourself into a corner, milking the same beer all night, waiting for someone to come talk to you."

His words seeped in through my anger. People did talk about parties at school all the time, and plenty went without being invited. I never thought to go—I knew I'd be as ostracized there as I was at school. But was I the one ostracizing myself?

"Kelvin has started us down the road to the next level of notecards," Mr. Griffin said. "He's working on an Identity Card, which focuses on who you are as a person."

"His card doesn't have a goal," Christy said.

"Of course it does. The goal is to strengthen his self-perception and to further develop the qualities he admires."

"How come there was no timeline?" Darnell asked.

"How many of you consider Kelvin generous now?"

All of my classmates raised their hands, and my neck grew hot.

"Timelines work great when there's a clear measurable, which does not exist here. Kelvin is taking a trait he already has and is working to expand it within himself. No matter how hard he works, he'll never exhaust the ability to grow his generosity."

"Then why not have the language of 'I intend to…' that other goals have?" Christy asked.

"That's the funny thing with traits. Just acknowledging them already makes them grow."

"I think we're all still pretty confused," Jarod said.

"Let me try again. Kelvin, did you read your card this morning?"

"Yes."

"What did you think about when you read, 'I am generous?'"

"Well, I thought of all the things I've been doing to help the rest of the class."

"How did you feel about those efforts in that moment?"

"I felt good about them, I guess."

"Did it make you more or less interested in giving your classmates additional help?"

"More."

"So you see, just by reading, 'I am generous,' Kelvin's generosity grew stronger."

"That's all these cards are, just an 'I am' statement?" Christy asked.

"No, we have to add steps."

"What should I put down?" I asked.

Mr. Griffin described the steps, and Jarod bust out laughing. At first, Christy sent him a scathing look, but before long, she and Darnell were laughing as well.

The only ones not laughing were Mr. Griffin, who could have been teaching trigonometry for all the emotion he was showing, and me, sitting there in stunned silence.

* * *

That night I took my notecard and phone into the bathroom. I locked the bathroom door, opened a radio app, and blasted the music from my phone so no one would overhear me.

And, honestly, so I wouldn't have to hear myself.

I stood in front of the bathroom mirror, took a quick look, and dropped my eyes to the card. This wouldn't do. I gritted my teeth, swallowed hard, and looked up again. I held my gaze for a full second before turning away.

Why was this so hard? I was just looking at myself in the mirror. I did this every day for crying out loud!

But not like this. Not really looking. Not facing myself.

I forced myself to face the mirror. After all, that stupid contract Mr. Griffin made me sign said that my math grade would plummet if I didn't do it. I was supposed to look myself in the eye, but I kept honing in on the mountain range of zits running across my forehead, the greasy shine covering my nose, the matted flop of hair on my head. *So disgusting.*

My chest tightened, my mouth felt pasty. Tears welled up in my eyes—*what was I, a crybaby?* I spat at my reflection, bit my lip, turned the music off, and reached for the door. *This is so dumb. Who am I kidding?*

The door slammed behind me.

"Kelvin, what's your problem?" Megan yelled out from her room.

"Shut up!" I slammed my bedroom door and crawled into my bed.

Chapter Eight

The Man in the Mirror

Next day, I spent the entire "math" class with my head in my notebook, doodling cubes over and over again. My teeth kept grabbing my lip until I ripped a piece of dead skin that made it bleed; then I licked the wound like a dog. Christy went on about the swim team in the background, but it was all a blur. And no one called my name, not even Mr. Griffin.

I wouldn't want to talk to me either.

When the bell finally rang, I didn't look up until I was sure my classmates had all filed out of the room. Once they were gone, I gathered my things as fast as I could.

"Rough night?" Mr. Griffin sat on his swivel chair, his feet up on his desk. His socks had a stupid reindeer on each ankle.

"Whatever." I slammed my notebook shut.

"Verbose today, I see."

Was he *trying* to piss me off?

"Oh, just leave me alone." I shoved my notebook into my bag. "It's bad enough you're going to flunk me in math for blowing off this stupid card."

"Flunk you? No, if you'll recall, the assignment is to spend five minutes a day working with your cards. Checking off the app was just a way for me to verify that you've done it. But one look at your face tells me you've hardly blown off your card."

"What do *you* know?"

Mr. Griffin held out his hand. "These scars came from punching my mirror the first time I tried to read an Identity Card."

"*You*? Really?"

Mr. Griffin shoved his fist in my face. Thin, pale lines crisscrossed his knuckles. "You couldn't do it either?"

He shook his head.

"So…how…?"

"I told you about my classmate, Scott, the artist who took his own life. He slit his wrists about a month after my bloody affair with the mirror." Mr. Griffin dropped his fist. "I didn't want that to be me."

A shiver ran up my spine. "Me neither. But…"

"But what?"

"I just can't," I said. "I can't do it. Even the thought of trying again makes my stomach turn."

"Then that means you *have* to do it." Mr. Griffin stood. "Fear is like a spotlight, shining on the precise areas where we need to grow." He pushed me toward the door. "Come on."

I followed Mr. Griffin down the hall, ignoring the fact that I was already late for physics. He stepped into the teacher's lounge. I hesitated at the door, then followed him in. No one was there except Coach Thomas, who was scarfing down a sandwich with headphones on.

"In here." Mr. Griffin held another door open.

"The bathroom? With *you*?" The only time I'd ever heard of a teacher bringing a student into the bathroom was on the front page of the paper.

"Yes. With *me*," he said, straight-faced. "*Now*."

I rolled my eyes and stepped into the bathroom. At least Mr. Griffin didn't lock the door. That would've been creepy.

"You have your card in there?" He pointed to my backpack.

"I ripped it up this morning on my way to school. It's in the cafeteria dumpster along with yesterday's meatball surprise."

"Then we'll wing it. Look in the mirror."

I lifted my head about an inch, then sank back down. "I can't."

"You don't like what you see there?"

The ball in my throat grew painful. "I *hate* what I see."

Mr. Griffin grabbed my chin and forced it up. "Face it."

"I don't wanna face it!" My eyes welled up, and my reflection became a blur.

"Kelvin, this guy in the mirror, he's all you've got."

"That sucks! Gimme someone else." I tried forcing my head to the side, but Mr. Griffin was too strong. All I saw in my reflection was an ugly loser with a face full of zits, who no one liked.

"It doesn't matter who you *wish* you were. Take a good look. That's the guy you've got to live with for the rest of your life!"

That's when I broke down, fell out of his grip, and collapsed on the floor. I sobbed like a baby for what felt like hours but was probably just a few minutes. Mr. Griffin sat next to me on the cold bathroom tiles and passed me some toilet paper to blow my nose.

His face softened, and he said, "As far as I can tell, you've got two options, Kelvin. You can continue hating yourself until it kills you, or you can find a way to change what you see."

"I've tried. You know how often my mom's dragged me off to the dermatologist?"

Mr. Griffin actually laughed. "I don't mean to change the look of your face. I mean to change what you see."

"You're not going to have me do one of those stupid things where I say over and over again, 'I'm beautiful' until I actually see my zits as beautiful, are you?"

"No, I want to change what you focus on so that you're so busy seeing what's truly beautiful about you that you hardly notice the zits."

"Me? Beautiful? Come on…"

"I'll demonstrate what I mean. Spend 10 seconds searching around the room for objects that are gray." Mr. Griffin counted off the seconds. "Stop. Now close your eyes and tell me, how many objects in the room do you remember that are red?"

"Red? I thought you told me to search for gray?"

"I did. But now I'm asking you for red. Keep your eyes closed. How many do you remember?"

"Just the label on my backpack, cause I know it's there."

"Now, open your eyes and tell me how many red things you see."

I pointed to the smoke detector, an information sticker about sexual abuse, and the reindeer on his socks. I could have gone on and on but didn't bother. "Is there a point to this stupid little game?"

"Why hadn't you seen all of that the first time?"

"Because you told me to look for gray."

"Precisely, but your eyes passed over the very same bathroom when you were scanning for gray things as they did when you looked for red. How come you didn't notice them?"

I shrugged. "It's not what I focused on, I guess."

"Exactly. Don't fool yourself into thinking that you see reality. The world is far too complex for us to take it all in. Rather, each of us tells our brains what to look for, and that's what we see."

"If that were the case, then each of us would be living in our own worlds."

"Exactly."

"But that's absurd."

"Is it? Tell me, when you look in the mirror, what's the first thing you see?"

"My zits."

Mr. Griffin tilted his head so he could look me straight in the eye. "Isn't that interesting? I barely notice them."

"You're just saying that cause you're my teacher."

"No, it's not just me, and I'll prove it."

"How are you going to do that?"

"I want you to post on social media, and ask a simple question, *'When you think of me, what are the first three words that come to mind?'* Tell them to be brutally honest."

"You want me to encourage people to make fun of me?"

"No, I want you to hear what people genuinely think of you. I think you'll be surprised." Mr. Griffin got to his feet. I waited for him to say more, but he turned and walked out of the bathroom.

So now I found myself sitting on the floor of the faculty bathroom, all by myself, my eyes no doubt swollen from crying. There was no way I was getting up and going to my next class like this. Did I really want to ask everyone what they thought of me? I knew the answer to that question. No way.

Then an image of Darnell with his numbered shirts ran through my mind. It took serious guts to suffer that humiliation. Could I not handle the same?

Before I lost my nerve, I took out my cell phone and posted Mr. Griffin's exact words.

* * *

All afternoon, I avoided checking my phone and even went so far as to turn off the Wi-Fi on my computer while I worked on my Catcher in the Rye essay.

But every time I tried thinking about Holden Caulfield, my mind wandered. I saw myself bawling on the floor of the faculty toilet. I saw Mr. Griffin's scarred knuckles. I even pictured his high school friend Scott, who I imagined had curly blond hair, lanky legs, and tattered jeans. All I really knew about him was that he was artistic. Was he smart? Funny? Did he see in himself whatever Mr. Griffin saw in him?

Then it hit me: he probably had no clue. I bet all he saw were his own version of zits.

After my fifth attempt at writing anything of logical significance on Mr. Caulfield, I knew it was time to face the question I'd been avoiding all day. What did others really think of me? I flipped on my Wi-Fi, and there were sixteen responses awaiting me.

The first response was from Derek, who never missed an opportunity to rub salt in an exposed wound. He wrote that the three words that came to mind for him were "Dweeb, dweeb, dweeb."

As I scrolled down, I saw his was the only insulting response. All of my Mastermind Group responded. Christy said, "Smart, helpful, and creative." Jarod also said *smart* but added *nice* and *good problem solver,* which wasn't technically one word, but a nice sentiment. Darnell wrote "skinny white boy," with a smiley, then wrote his real answer of "friendly, determined, and smart."

For some reason, seeing smart written over and over, irked me, despite the fact that I'd always prided myself on my intelligence. But no one mentioned zits, nor did anyone other than Derek say anything obnoxious.

My mother wrote funny, curious, and conscientious. Even my sister was complimentary; she put sweet, clever, and strong (really I was a total weakling, but I suppose I seemed strong to a preteen).

Other responses included considerate, interesting, articulate, and geek, which came from one of my hacker camp friends, so it wasn't a putdown.

Was this really how others saw me, or were they all just being nice? I'd told people to be brutally honest, but even if the first word that came to their mind was zits, would they share that?

Still, there was no denying that it felt nice reading all of these things about myself. Even Derek's dweeb comment didn't seem like such a big deal next to everything else.

And what if they were telling the truth? Why couldn't I see myself that way?

I pulled out a fresh notecard. It was time to try this again. I sucked in a long, deep breath, and wrote a new Identity Card to replace the one now rotting in the dumpster. The image of Scott lying in a pool of his own blood kept popping into my mind, pushing me to write each trait.

I shoved the new card in my pocket, opened the radio app on my phone, and before I knew it, found myself in the bathroom. *Again.*

I blasted the music and locked the door like the previous night, hoping that this time would be different—that *I* would be different.

The card was burning in my pocket, so I pulled it out and gripped it in both hands. I swallowed hard and turned toward the mirror.

My stomach clenched, and my chest caved in. *Damn loser!* I turned away and grabbed the door handle. An image of Darnell in his numbered shirts, taking everyone's insults because he knew it would make him stronger, flashed through my mind. If he could suffer that humiliation from others, the least I could do was face myself. I mustered my courage and grasped the card.

The whole notecard exercise was supposed to take only five minutes a day, but by the time five minutes had passed, I hadn't even begun. The first words, the ones that got Jarod laughing, just wouldn't come out.

This is crazy. They were so simple, and no one could hear.

Hell, if I couldn't speak them to myself, how could I ever hope to speak like this to anyone else?

OK, I'm going to do it. Count of three. 1, 2, 3. I looked up, caught my eyes, and whispered, "I love you, Kelvin," then quickly sank to the floor.

And there I was, again, crumpled on cold bathroom tiles, crying like a baby.

Why did this hurt so much?

If Jarod did it, he'd quickly say "I love you Jarod" like it was nothing. Would it be so much easier for him because he wouldn't take the assignment seriously, or because he simply loved himself more? For some reason, this thought got me angry. I hit the floor, punched the wall. *Stop being such a loser!*

I turned to the list on my notecard, but the words were a blur. I wiped my eyes and tried again.

I stood, faced the mirror, and forced myself to hold steady. *Ignore the zits. Focus on what's inside, on what matters.*

The first trait on my card was generosity. I said, "You, Kelvin are generous." That part was easy—the rest was not. I vividly recalled the bizarre dialog in class when Mr. Griffin had explained all of this.

Jarod raised his hand but didn't wait to be called on to speak. "Why is Kelvin talking to himself in the third person? Why say, "You are generous, rather than I am generous?"

"Even more than the Outcome Cards, the Identity Cards work on the subconscious level," Mr. Griffin replied. "The third person allows you greater separation from your own baggage, and so it resonates in your mind more like an objective, outside opinion. It's speaking in the language of the subconscious, which leads me to the next step. Kelvin, you'll need to state three reasons why you know your statement is true."

"Why?" Jarod asked.

"Because evidence is the building block of belief. Each day of your lives you've seen the sun rise, so by now you believe with your full heart that it will rise again tomorrow."

"What does that have to do with Kelvin?" Darnell asked.

"If he keeps feeding his mind evidence that he's generous, he'll come to believe it as fact. It will become a core part of his identity, of how he sees himself."

"So each day I have to come up with new evidence?" I asked.

"Ideally. That doesn't mean you can never repeat something you've used before. But the more evidence you provide, the more you hammer it in."

So now I needed evidence of my generosity. My mind went to my three classmates. I'd helped them all, hadn't I?

I looked back at the mirror. "You, Kelvin, are generous. You made two flyers for Jarod, you made a video for Christy, and you helped get Darnell a treadmill."

That went OK, but the next step was ridiculous.

"Once you've listed off the evidence," Mr. Griffin had said, "I want you to come up with a new nickname."

"A nickname?" I asked.

"Yes. You'll say, 'In fact, you're so generous, you're really…,' and then you have to plug in a nickname that encapsulates that trait."

"Like a superhero?"

"Precisely. We're looking for an emotional anchor for this trait in your subconscious. The more fun you make it, the more it will stick. For instance, I could say that I'm a 'builder of successful businesses,' but that's boring. So I call myself a 'success doctor.' I'm also a love machine, an ironman, and a host of other things that I say to myself each day."

I stared at myself in the mirror. I just had to get through this. "In fact, you're so generous, you're really…"

Really what? I needed something fun, something that would encapsulate my generosity. But if I was ever in a not-fun mood, it was now. What could I say?

A tap-tap reverberated through the bathroom. "Kelvin?" my mother called. "Is everything OK?"

Though my heart thumped, she probably hadn't heard me crying or punching the walls. But I *had* been in here for an awfully long time. Plus, she'd seen my social media post, even responded to it, so she knew something was going on. "Yeah, Mom, everything's fine."

"Alright, honey….Let me know if you need me." Her footsteps grew quiet as she returned to her room.

I had to get through this card and out of the bathroom already.

I tried again. "In fact, you're so generous, you're really…Captain Generous."

OK, it was lame, and I knew it. I'd try to do better tomorrow. But the words nonetheless made me giggle.

Onto the next trait. "Kelvin, you are sensitive." This one was harder. What had I done that was sensitive? I'd said supportive things to Darnell when he started taping numbers on his chest, rather than making fun of him like others did. Also, I'd cried when telling myself 'I love you.' I guess that was sensitivity. What else?

It took me an hour before I'd gone through all the traits on the card. Worse, I was spent. Who knew that talking to yourself could be so draining? I flopped on my bed and passed out, still fully dressed, shoes and all.

Chapter Nine

Risk and Reward

Reading the cards the next morning went much faster. It had to, or I would have been late for school. Ahh...the power of deadlines.

On Wednesdays, Darnell and I had lunch together. All he had on his tray were an undressed salad and an apple. I kept my bologna sandwich half hidden from him behind my thermos, as if that would make a difference.

"Down to 235 I see. Wow, that's like a pound a day."

"Yeah." He grinned, but his voice was flat. His grin collapsed as he looked at his salad.

"Aren't you hungry?"

"Kinda...but no pain, no gain, right?" Darnell pulled out his card and read it to himself before taking a bite out of his apple.

"How do you know if it's too much pain?"

"I dunno. I just wanna hit the goal on my card." He put the card away and wiped his forehead. "I can suck it up for another few days. I've gotten this far, haven't I?"

* * *

Christy burst into fifth period, cheering that her team won their latest swim meet, making them 3-0 for the season.

I didn't want to offer a report. I wasn't embarrassed to share—I wouldn't tell them the full details of my break down. It's just that I still didn't get the point of what I was doing and definitely didn't believe the words I was saying. So maybe it was embarrassment. I felt like the loser in class with the dork assignment.

Fortunately, Jarod had news. "I reached this guy, Bill. He runs a big landscaping business a couple of towns over. He didn't have a lot of time for me, but he offered me a deal."

"What's the deal?" Mr. Griffin asked.

"He says he's got a big job he's working this Saturday. He can use another set of capable hands. If I'm willing to come work the full day for nothing, then I can ask him as many questions as I like while we work."

"What did you say?"

"I wanted to think about it but didn't tell him that. So I told him I've got a job that I'd see if I could move to another time. I'm supposed to get back to him with an answer today."

"Why the hesitation?"

"I've got my own jobs I can be working Saturday and actually get paid. I can push them off a day, but that means I'll be working like a dog on Sunday. No doubt Bill will work me hard on Saturday too, and he expects me to do the entire thing for *free*."

"It sounds like you've made up your mind. Why didn't you tell him 'no' on the spot?"

"Truthfully, I wanted to wait until I spoke with you, Mr. Griffin. Do you think I'd be making a mistake?"

Wow. Jarod seeking out the advice of a teacher? These cards were certainly having an effect on *him*.

Mr. Griffin smiled. "You really want to know what I think?"

"Yes, I do."

"I think you'd be making a *giant* mistake."

"So you think I should work for free?"

"Free? Absolutely not."

"So what do I do? Go back and see if he'll pay me for the day?"

"No, his offer was clear. Take him up on his offer and don't ask for any money for your work."

Jarod laughed. "Didn't you just say I shouldn't work for free?"

"No one's asking you to. Never be afraid to give value to get value. He's offering you something potentially far more valuable than money: his advice."

Jarod crossed his arms. "How do I know what that's worth?"

"You don't."

"Sooo…"

"There's a concept I want you all to learn called Asymmetrical Risk/Reward."

"You finally gonna teach us some math?" Jarod asked.

"Not exactly. Asymmetrical Risk/Reward means you want to put yourself in situations where you risk little to potentially gain much."

"Like betting on long shots?" Jarod asked.

"No, more like betting on favorites with long shot odds."

"They never give that option at the track," Jarod said.

"No, they don't. The tracks and the casinos will always stack the odds against you, whether you're betting on favorites or long shots. But in life, odds can vary greatly."

"Like how?" Christy asked.

"You experienced two opposite examples of Asymmetrical Risk/Reward, Christy, when you lost a swim coach, and then when you gained a new one."

"I don't follow," she said.

"You lost your coach to a drunk driver. Getting behind the wheel when he'd been drinking put the driver and others at tremendous risk. Yet the reward, the pleasure of a few drinks, was minimal."

Christy recoiled.

"Then you found a great new coach by calling the top swim coaches in the world. The risk was negligible—it only took a few hours of your time—but the rewards were tremendous."

Jarod pursed his lips. "So you're saying that my risk here is just a day of lost wages. If Bill has nothing valuable to teach me, then I've worked for nothing, which is no big deal. But if he has something worthwhile to share, if he can help me reach my goal, then I could eventually make thousands of dollars from that one day's work."

Mr. Griffin nodded. "Ask any successful business person how much their biggest mistakes have cost them. You'll be shocked by the numbers they give. If you can learn from another's mistakes, you can save yourself years of hardship. The flip side is also true. It probably took him years to learn his most profitable lessons. And you can get all that for one day of sweat."

Jarod pulled out his phone. "I'll do it."

* * *

I continued reading my cards twice a day, checking off the app each time. While it was never quite easy, I didn't break down like I had that first time. I became more creative with my nicknames and started to enjoy the exercise.

Captain Generosity gave way to Generosity Man, which didn't sound quite as cool, but at least had a theme song ("generosity man, generosity man, giving all that generosity can"). And then there was Sensitivity Superstar, which made me think of the Emmy's.

That Friday night, I babysat again. I asked Megan what kind of pizza she wanted, though I knew she'd say mushroom. "Want to get garlic sticks too?" I asked.

Megan avoided looking at me. "Whatever."

"Helloooo. Want them or not?"

Megan's shoulders rose and fell. I squatted to get a better look and saw her eyes were red. By unspoken rule, we left each other to do our own thing when I babysat, but I had a sudden inspiration.

"Hey, it's going to be a half hour before the pizza gets here. Want to go for a walk?"

"A walk?" She rolled her eyes at me. "Really?"

"Why not?"

"Well for one, it's freezing out."

"It's not so bad, and it's a clear night. Come on."

"What are you up to?"

"Nothing. I just think it would be nice to go for a walk."

Megan shrugged, but then said, "Okay, I guess," and got up to get her coat while I called in the pizza.

It really was cold out. I tightened the scarf around my neck. "How are things going?" I asked.

"Fine."

What did I expect, that she was going to open up the moment I tried to act brotherly? "You having a hard time?" I tried again.

She crossed her arms. "A bit, I guess."

"Want to talk about it?"

"Not really."

Had we been inside the house, I probably would have given up at this point. But even if we turned around now, we'd have to walk home together. I'd feel like an idiot doing it in silence. "I had a tough time when I was your age," I said.

"You did?"

Where had she been? There were only five years between us. Surely even then she was old enough to notice I spent most of my time alone on my computer. Then the truth slapped me in the face. She wouldn't have seen that, she was only eight at the time. *I* was the one who should have noticed she was now on her own most of the time. This wasn't the first time her eyes had been red from crying. *Where had I been?*

The answer came screaming in. I'd been so absorbed in my own pity party that I'd spared no attention for her struggles.

It's strange. I'd tried to be there for her tonight, tried asking her about her hard time, and she bottled up. Then I mentioned my own, and she suddenly seemed interested. I didn't understand it, but decided to take the opening.

"Oh yeah, seventh grade was the worst for me. I still don't have as many friends as I'd like, but back then I had none."

"Why not?" she asked.

"I don't know. It's like when I was young, all the boys were more or less the same. Then when we hit middle school, suddenly I felt different."

"How?"

"Well, my interests weren't theirs. I was into computers. They were into girls."

Megan laughed. "You weren't into girls?"

I laughed along with her. "I was, but none of them ever seemed to notice me. It's like there were suddenly all of these rules about how you had to look, how you had to talk, or whatever. But no one ever explained the rules to me, and the ones I did get seemed stupid."

"I totally know what you mean."

"In elementary school, we were all friends with each other. Middle school was a lot bigger—there were so many more kids. All these groups started forming, and before I knew it, I was on the outside."

"Yeah, that's how it feels with me." Megan wrung her hands together as if debating something, then said, "A bunch of girls are over at Joanna's tonight for a sleepover."

"You and Joanna used to be such good friends."

Megan nodded.

"But she didn't invite you, and you're feeling left out."

"Yeah."

We came around the block back to our house. Inspiration struck again. "What do you say we make a huge vat of popcorn and watch *The Princess Bride* tonight?"

"Can we do it in our PJs?"

"Absolutely."

We'd reached our front door. For the first time I could remember, Megan hugged me. "That sounds great."

* * *

The next morning I took my notecards into the bathroom. Though I still locked the door and turned on the radio, it didn't feel as necessary as on that first night.

I looked at myself in the mirror and, for the first time, had little difficulty holding my gaze. I said, "Kelvin, I love you," and laughed at the silliness of it. The awkwardness was still there, but it was no longer so difficult.

When thinking of examples of my sensitivity, I reflected on my walk with Megan and the fun night we shared.

When I read off the card about how funny I was, I thought of all the moments I got Megan to laugh after we'd already finished the movie and sat up eating ice cream and telling stories.

In fact, for each trait on my card, something about Megan came up. And the strange thing was that I felt great. Here I'd spent a Friday night doing exactly what I'd tried desperately to avoid for years—sitting at home with my kid sister while the cool kids at school partied—and I'd had a great time.

After reading through all of my card (which only took ten minutes this time), I decided to visit Darnell. He hadn't reached out since that night I'd blown him off a week earlier. Suddenly, I wanted to connect with him and see how much progress he was making toward his goal.

I made it over to his house in the early afternoon and found him watching football with his family, as usual. While none were quite as heavy as Darnell, everyone in his family was obese. All of them sat on the couch watching the game, except for Darnell, who chugged away on his treadmill. He wasn't quite running—I doubted Darnell had run since middle school—but he kept a fast walk.

"Hi Kelvin," his mom said. "Nachos?"

Darnell's mom had always been incredibly warm and welcoming whenever I'd been to their house, and the woman knew how to cook. Now she extended a plate of nachos dripping with cheddar cheese and flecked with bacon. I didn't like the idea of eating junk food in front of Darnell, but I also didn't want to be rude and refuse, especially given how good the nachos looked. "Thanks, Mrs. Jones." I helped myself to a small serving, poured some picante salsa on the side, and plopped myself onto a plush armchair.

Darnell's eyes followed the plate of nachos.

"How's it going, Darnell?" I asked.

"Good. Five more pounds to go."

"I've never seen him work so hard." Mrs. Jones sipped her Mountain Dew.

Darnell smiled at the praise, but the smile only lasted a moment. I didn't think a 230-pound man could appear starved, but that's exactly how he looked. There was a desperation in his eyes, as if he hadn't eaten in weeks. His father ate a slice of sausage pizza, and his sister had already moved onto ice cream for dessert. But Darnell kept his eyes on the TV as though it were a bull's eye.

I stayed until the end of the first game—Darnell walking on the treadmill the entire time—and I left marveling at his willpower.

* * *

On Monday, Darnell came in another two pounds lighter, but it wasn't just his weight that had dropped. Dark caves sunk under his eyes, and his skin was pasty—like raw brownie batter.

Mr. Griffin took one look at him, then turned his attention away. "Jarod, how did it go with Bill on Saturday?"

"OK, I think."

"You think?"

"He worked me hard and didn't say much."

"Any value in what he did say?"

"Not sure."

"Tell us about it."

"Well, I showed up at 7:30 Saturday morning at the address he gave me, just like we agreed. The houses out there are like four times the size of the ones around here, and the yard was at least ten times the size of the ones I normally work on. I saw the truck from his landscaping company in the driveway, so I knew it was the right address. There wasn't any work being done in the front, so I went around to the back of the house. The backyard was even bigger, with a pool and a whole decked out patio, but I didn't see any work being done back there either.

"So I returned to the front and rang the bell. Bill answered the door himself. Turns out it was his house. Even though I was on time, he said, 'Glad to see you're finally here. Let's go.'"

In middle school, Jarod had starred in all the school plays. He gave up drama when he'd given up all other school activities, but he still had a knack for doing voices. He portrayed Bill as having a rough, somewhat Italian accent.

"We got into his truck, but as we drove off, he looked at my pickup. 'You got a snow plow for that thing?' When I told him no, he said, 'Get one.'

"I've got a decent snow blower, and I told him I never wanted to spend the money on a plow for the truck, especially when I still needed a snow blower for the walkways anyway.

"This just pissed him off. He said, 'One shnook pushing a snow blower is no different than another shnook pushing a snow blower. A 10-year-old can do the same work as you for half the price.'

"When I told him that I make more money on snow days than any other day of the year, he said, 'How much?' I told him, and he just said, 'peanuts.'

"He said, '99% of the time no one values manual laborers. The exception is emergencies. When there's a heavy snowstorm, a guy with a truck and a plow is more important than the governor. That's when guys like you and me make our money.'

"I said there's only so much time during a snow day."

"He waved me off. 'That's why you don't even worry about the piddly jobs. If someone asks you to plow their walk, you tell them you'll get to it once the snow stops falling and all the driveways are clear. Then you watch and see what happens. If some hysterical businessman says he needs his parking lot plowed out, and he's a mile away, what do you do?'

"I book it over there."

"'The hell you do. You tell him absolutely sir, you'll be happy to get to it in a couple of hours when you're in that part of town. Then you watch and see what happens.'

"He'll go nuts."

"'Exactly...'"

"Most of the day the equipment was too loud for us to hear each other. When we got a quiet moment, he barely even answered my questions but kept spitting out random pieces of advice. Whenever I asked him to explain anything, he would say, 'You just watch and see what happens.'"

"So are you going to buy the plow for your truck?" Mr. Griffin asked.

"I don't know. It's going to cost me thousands of dollars out of my college fund. What do you think, Mr. Griffin?"

"I know little about landscaping. Did it strike you that Bill knew what he was talking about?"

"His house was certainly nice enough. I expect he does know. It's a big expense, but it will last me for years. I can do a lot more driveways with a truck plow." Jarod slapped his desk. "I'm going to do it."

* * *

Tuesday night, my mom made my favorite: homemade ravioli with mushrooms. By the time she finished cooking, flour covered the countertops, two sticky pots sat on the stove, and chopped mushroom bits lay scattered about.

Megan brought her latest art project to the table; she hadn't done that since she was in the second grade. I knew she'd want compliments and was nervous to see what she'd made. But it turned out I had no reason to worry.

"Wow," I said.

"You're just saying that..." Megan shrank.

"No, really, those strawberries look good enough to pick off the page. They remind me of the ones at Golder's Farm."

She danced in her seat. "That's what I was thinking of when I drew them. You really think it's good?"

"No, I think it's cruel. Golder's won't open for picking until June."

Megan's face lit up. "Thanks, Kelvin."

After dinner, our dishes piled up in the sink. Megan went off to her room, and Dad grabbed the newspaper and headed to the den. Mom pulled out her pink gloves from under the sink. She stood to face the mountain of dishes and sighed.

"How about I do the dishes tonight." Did I really say that? I hated doing dishes.

Mom turned around, her face frozen in shock.

"Gimme the gloves." I stretched out my hand and she hesitated. "Come on, Mom. You can dry, okay?"

Mom shook her head and woke out of her shock. "Um… okay."

She picked a towel from the drawer and took the first plate from my hand. "This reminds me of when Dad and I first got married. Dad had a lot more time on his hands when he was finishing his doctorate. He used to wash dishes, and I would dry."

"Was this in Boston?"

"Yeah. We had this tiny little studio apartment with a kitchen small enough to fit into your closet."

I soaped up the first pot. "What did you do when Dad was studying?"

"I took classes at the museum of art. That's when I painted the snowy landscape in the hallway."

I stopped and turned to face my mom. "You painted that?" How did I not know that? "I thought you got it at a gallery or something."

Mom blushed. "I must have told you…"

I shrugged and turned back to the sink. I probably hadn't paid attention – this was turning out to be a theme. "Did Dad paint something too?" It was hard to imagine, but then again, I hadn't known about Mom.

Mom cackled and almost dropped the heavy pot I'd just passed her. "Dad? No," she said, "But we first met at the art museum."

My shoulders clenched. I should have known this story. But I didn't. "Tell me…"

"Some famous art guy Smithy or Smithers or something came to the museum to talk about Monet when I was in my last year of college and just getting interested in painting. Dad had already started his PhD, and I think needed a break from reading so many biology papers." Mom grabbed a handful of forks and ran the towel along each one as she spoke. "He said he just 'happened' to sit next to me. I think he did it on purpose. The lecturer was late, so we got to talking."

"And you liked him?" I'm sure that sounded wrong. I was just surprised anyone could find my dad attractive. He always looked so… dorky. His hair was all over the place, he had dandruff and seemed to dress a decade behind the times.

"He was a great listener. He asked me all about the art in the museum and barely said anything as I told him about my favorite artists and their different painting styles." Mom's hands grew still, and her eyes looked up in reverie. "After the talk, we walked around the museum, and I showed him my favorite pieces. He was so happy to hear my thoughts. I liked that."

"So then you started dating?"

"No." Mom giggled. "I thought he was too nerdy."

I waited for her to finish the forks then passed her the knives. "So what happened?"

"He kept asking to spend time together, and he was nice enough, so I went. Then, I don't know—he grew on me."

"How?"

"He was thoughtful. He took me to his favorite Mexican place, and when we got there, he asked the waitress all about her son. Dad knew the boy was sick and had been doing research in the medical library at the university to try and help. Then he left the busboy this big tip. He was this immigrant from somewhere in Africa who barely spoke a word of English. People usually ignore guys like him." Dad still tipped busboys. It hadn't occurred to me no one else I knew did that.

Mom laid the glasses upside down to dry on the countertop. "After a while, he looked different to me…"

"Different how?"

Mom tipped her head toward her shoulder like a little girl. "I thought he was cute. We never officially dated, but one day Dad brought me to the art museum, making up some story about a newly acquired sculpture. On our way to the new exhibits gallery, we walked through the Impressionists section. Dad stopped in front of the Monet painting, and that's when I noticed that the words 'Marry Me' were written with pink rose petals on the floor."

"Monet was your favorite," I said.

Mom nodded—her grin illuminated her face.

* * *

107

On Wednesday, Christy and I were the only students in class when the bell rang. We waited a few minutes, but neither Darnell nor Jarod showed up. Strange, given that I'd passed them both in the halls earlier in the day.

Finally, Christy said, "What's been going on with you, Kelvin?"

I had yet to give any updates in class. I got the impression that Mr. Griffin very intentionally had not drawn attention to me. I glanced up at him before responding, but he gestured for me to go ahead.

"I've been feeling great." The words left my lips of their own accord, but felt true. It was easier to share now that it was just Christy listening. I knew she wouldn't laugh at me like Jarod. Darnell wouldn't laugh either, but my stomach clenched at the thought of talking about how good I felt in front of someone who looked so miserable.

I told Christy about my experience with my sister on Friday night, about going to Darnell's on Saturday, and about helping my mother with the dishes the night before.

"But you've always been quick in this class to offer your help," Christy said. "Why is that such a change?"

"I don't know. I feel the shift, but I can't put my finger on exactly why."

"I bet you can," Mr. Griffin said.

I hesitated a moment, then nodded. "I guess I was so filled with self-pity before that I didn't have time for anyone else's difficulties. No," I corrected myself, "I had time, I just didn't notice."

The door opened, and Jarod walked in. "Where have you been?" Mr. Griffin asked, his voice more concerned than accusatory.

"The nurse's office."

"You look OK," Christy said.

"It's not me. I brought Darnell. He passed out during lunch."

Chapter Ten

Smarter, Not Harder

D arnell dragged himself into class on Wednesday. It was the first time in weeks that he didn't wear a number across his chest. "I failed," he said.

"That remains to be seen," Mr. Griffin said. "What is your weight?"

"230." Darnell slumped into his chair like a wet rag. "Today's my deadline, and I'm three pounds over."

"You lost twelve pounds," Christy said. "That's remarkable."

"More," Jarod said, "you dropped sixteen pounds since Thanksgiving."

"I still missed my goal. It's like what Mr. Griffin said to you Jarod, if you hit your goal, you build momentum. You miss it, you lose it."

"What he said," Jarod leaned forward, "is that if the deadline passes and you've missed your goal, you should still congratulate yourself for all the progress you made. He just told me not to give up before the deadline, which I almost did."

"I tried to push myself to hit my deadline. I figured if I didn't drink yesterday I could lose an additional pound or two in water weight. Look where it landed me. The nurse made me drink like a gallon of water, then my mom made me eat when I got home. She said 'no more of this craziness,' and she stood over me while I finished everything."

"Still," Jarod said, "now's the time to see all the progress you've made. Not to beat yourself up."

"It's too hard. I don't want to keep doing this."

"Nor should you," Mr. Griffin said.

Was Mr. Griffin really telling Darnell to give up?

"No?" Darnell asked.

"Absolutely not. It was madness." Did Mr. Griffin blame himself for one of his students passing out during school? Did he come to realize that all of these steps he was teaching us were misguided?

But what about all of the progress that Christy and Jarod had made? What about my own opening up? What about Darnell losing twelve pounds? Was he really going to throw in the towel now? I called out, "You can't mean that, Mr. Griffin?"

"I do mean it. Darnell has been on a burnout path for weeks."

"He's been doing great," Jarod said.

Mr. Griffin shook his head. "It was never sustainable."

"You realized this the whole time?" Christy asked.

"I did."

"And you didn't say anything?"

"Of course not. I'm here to teach. Darnell's just learned a lesson he'll never forget. He wouldn't have gotten that if I'd interfered."

"What's the lesson?" Christy asked.

"That I'm just a fat guy," Darnell said, "and that's all I'll ever be."

Mr. Griffin laughed. "No, Darnell, that's not the lesson I wished to impart."

"Then what's the lesson?"

"Work smarter, not harder."

"Huh?" Darnell said.

"Work smarter, not harder."

"I don't follow."

"Since Thanksgiving, you've lost sixteen pounds, all from willpower. Willpower is a wonderful thing, and by using it, you strengthen it. But willpower can only get you so far. It's not a sustainable strategy."

"Why not?" Christy asked.

"You burn yourself out. If Darnell hadn't burned out now, I'm sure he would have done so come exams. There's only so much we can pile on our plates and continue to will our way through."

"Then what's a sustainable strategy?" Darnell asked.

"That's what you must discover. It will be different in each case. The answers are all within your reach, and if you can't see them, I'm certain your Mastermind Group will."

"So what do I do now?" Darnell asked.

"First thing, write a new card. Never let one card expire without replacing it with the next, or you really *will* lose your momentum. That's especially true now with Christmas and New Year's around the corner. You don't want a repeat of Thanksgiving, do you?"

"No. I never want to go back there." Darnell pulled out a pen. "OK, fine. I'll write another card." He received one from Mr. Griffin. "What should it say?"

When Mr. Griffin remained silent, Christy said, "Maybe you should write a more realistic goal? Like when I aim to lower my lap times, I pick a number that feels challenging but not outrageous. Maybe fifteen pounds in one month is too much to be, as Mr. Griffin says, 'sustainable?'"

"How much do you think?" Darnell asked.

"Maybe just one to two pounds a week?" Christy offered.

Darnell's sighed and turned to Mr. Griffin. "Is that what you are suggesting?"

"No, Darnell."

"Then what?"

Yet again, Mr. Griffin remained silent.

"Why won't you help?" Darnell pounded his desk.

"I am helping. I'm helping you to realize that between yourself and your Mastermind Group, you have all the resources you need to answer this question."

Darnell turned to us. "Any of you have anything else to add?"

"I don't know everything that should go on the card," Jarod said, "but maybe we can start with what we do have."

"Like what?"

"Well, the cards have a goal, a date, and the steps. Let's fill out what we can, and then brainstorm the rest."

Darnell said, "OK, I can do that. The date is easy. I can give myself another 30 days. Christy, I hear what you're saying about setting easier goals, and truthfully, I don't have the strength to do another 15 pounds, not now. But I can't get excited about one to two pounds a week."

"Why not?" Christy asked.

"Remember, my original goal had been to lose 70 pounds during this school year. I'm not ready to give up on that yet. If I don't make real progress now, when I've got the support of all of you, I don't know when I'll ever do it."

"I don't want to see you hurt yourself again," Christy said.

"Neither do I. So I'm going to put down ten pounds over the next thirty days. That's half the pace I've been on since Thanksgiving."

Darnell started writing. When he finished, he said, "My card now reads:

I intend to weigh 220 pounds or less by January 22. To accomplish this, I will:

There was a long, dead pause. Darnell's list hadn't worked so well for him before, and he clearly had no idea what to replace it with. "Anyone have any thought what I should put down as steps?" he asked.

Mr. Griffin still said nothing. He'd been overweight himself, and I felt certain that he could guide Darnell on a healthier, more successful path. Yet, he preferred to offer Darnell another one of his *lessons learned the hard way.*

When no one came forward with any answers, Jarod said, "I have no idea what you should put down, but Christmas Eve is tomorrow night, so you'll want to hurry up and get the answers you need."

I read the terror on Darnell's face. I could only imagine what Christmas dinner would be like at his house. With his willpower clearly drained, and his mother now firmly against his diet, it was going to be hard to get through it without his waistline ballooning all over again.

I also didn't have a strategy to get him moving forward, but I felt a strong urge to help him develop one. "How about if I come over after school today, Darnell, and we try to figure this out together?"

The tight ridge in his brow relaxed. "That would be great."

* * *

"Can you believe Mr. Griffin saw you failing and didn't say anything?" I said as Darnell and I walked back to his house that afternoon. "You could have hurt yourself."

"I did. I bumped my head when I passed out. It's still sore."

"Why didn't you mention that?"

"Guess I was feeling humiliated enough."

"People give you hell for it?"

"Yeah, Derek hasn't picked on me in weeks, ever since Jarod stood up for me, but now it's like Christmas came early for him. He kept pretending to pass out in front of me at lunch today. He also asked, loud enough for everyone to hear, why I didn't have the number on my chest. Asked if I'd given up."

"You'll wipe that smile off his face when you come back from vacation five pounds lighter."

"*If* I come back from vacation five pounds lighter, you mean. Like I said, I can't keep this up."

"Mr. Griffin lost all this weight himself. You'd think he'd offer you more advice." My fists clenched. "From his smug look, it's obvious he knows where you're going wrong, but doesn't want to tell you."

"He's right about one thing, though. If I do figure it out, I'm not easily going to forget." Why was I getting so much more upset about this than Darnell was himself? "And he did leave us a clue," Darnell said.

"'Smarter, not harder' hardly strikes me as a clue. He said himself, it can mean something different in each circumstance."

"So what does it mean in mine? Come on, Kelvin, you're the bright one."

I didn't like that claim that I was the bright one. Darnell wasn't stupid, and he showed this past month that his will was far stronger than my own. I wouldn't have pushed myself until I passed out. No way. Besides, I couldn't think of an answer.

"OK," I said, "we don't know what the answer is, but we know what it's not. If Mr. Griffin is right—that willpower is finite—then what I saw on Saturday has got to be a willpower killer."

"What did you see?"

"I saw everyone eating your favorite foods, while you walked on a treadmill trying not to notice."

"The worst was when you came over and started eating the nachos under my nose."

"Sorry about that. It's not easy to refuse your mom or her cooking."

"Tell me about it. I go through that every day."

"It looked like it took all of your strength to keep your eyes on the TV."

"And then some." We'd reached Darnell's house. As we stepped in, he asked, "You want a snack?" Already his mind was on food.

"What have you got?"

"Ice cream, chips, soda. Whatever you want."

Was Darnell really going to give me crap about eating nachos in front of him and then offer me ice cream? Even if he did offer, there was no way I was going to take it. Not now. "What do you have that we can both eat?"

"Nothing."

"What about an apple?"

He shook his head.

"You've got to have something. Show me."

Together the two of us went through the fridge, the freezer, the pantry. We found six flavors of ice cream, three kinds of candy bars, four varieties of chips, and three different sodas. The only vegetables I saw were a head of lettuce and a tomato, which Darnell said they put on their burgers. Fruits were completely non-existent, not counting the packets of fruit leather in the pantry.

"Did you tell your mom you wanted healthier snacks?"

"Yeah, that's why she bought the fruit leathers. But I read the label, and they have almost as much sugar as the candy bars."

This was worse than I thought. "Remember what Mr. Griffin told Jarod about alignment?"

"You mean with his girlfriend?"

"Exactly. It seems to me that you and your family are misaligned."

Darnell sighed. "That's true. And passing out yesterday didn't help. Now my mom's convinced that I'm going to kill myself with the diet."

"That's right. It's madness." Darnell's mom walked into the kitchen and planted her hand on his shoulder. "A boy like him not eating or drinking for days. What's that going to achieve? No one can keep that up. And the hours he spends on that treadmill..." She cast a glance at me now. The treadmill had been my idea.

Had the accusations come from a friend, I could easily have responded. But no way was I going to talk back to Mrs. Jones, especially in her home.

Darnell however, had no such compunctions. "I don't want to be fat all my life."

"You're a big boy. It's nothing to be ashamed of."

"I'm not just big. Don't you see I'm unhealthy, Mom?"

"Unhealthy?" His mom threw her hands in the air. "It's this diet that's unhealthy. When did you ever pass out after eating a good meal?"

"I used to be out of breath just going to class. I don't want to live this way."

"If you want to lose weight go ahead. But you don't have to be so obsessed about it. It's dangerous."

The veins in Darnell's forehead throbbed. "Mom, not again."

Suddenly, I had an inspiration and turned to Mrs. Jones. "I completely agree with you."

Darnell's head jerked back in surprise.

His mom said, "See, even Kelvin agrees. This diet is nuts."

"Exactly," I said. "That's the problem we were trying to solve today, how Darnell can continue to lose weight, without doing anything dangerous."

Darnell's anger softened. His mom's brow rose in confusion, as though trying to figure out if she'd been tricked.

"One thing we were just wondering was whether it would be possible to get healthier snacks in the house?" I said.

"Look, I've told Darnell, if he wants to do the shopping, he's welcome to."

Darnell rolled his eyes. "Come on, Mom, obviously I'm not going to—."

"Great," I said. "I'll come with you."

Darnell's mouth dropped open. "You want to do our shopping?"

I always hated it when my mom sent me out to buy groceries, but now the prospect of going shopping sounded fun. "Why not? It can't be any harder than fasting, right?"

Darnell shrugged.

His mom patted his cheek. "Great, I'll give you a list."

She wrote down everything she needed onto her kitchen pad. Darnell looked over her shoulder and said, "But Mom, this is all the stuff we normally buy."

"If you want to get other things, go ahead. But I'm not going to change how I cook just because you do the shopping."

Darnell groaned. "Then it's pointless."

"What if we did the cooking?" I asked.

Mrs. Jones looked down the end of her nose at me. "The two of you are going to do all of our cooking?"

I bit my lip. We were in winter break now, so we'd have the time if we wanted to. But did I really want to spend half my vacation cooking? "We'll do it tonight."

"You boys want to give me a night off, I'll take it. Heaven knows I'll be cooking more than enough the next couple of days. I'll give you a list of things to buy for me for Christmas dinner, but you're welcome to buy anything you want to cook tonight."

"Sounds good," I said. "Darnell?"

He looked from me to his mother. In the end, he shrugged and said, "Deal."

"Great," his mom said. "I'll go get you my credit card."

Darnell leaned over to me. "You know how to cook?"

"No. You?"

He shook his head. What had we just gotten ourselves into?

It took us almost an hour of walking around the supermarket to fill Mrs. Jones' Christmas dinner list. It would have taken a quarter that long if we hadn't kept picking things up, discussing whether they'd be good to make for dinner, and putting them back.

"Pasta?" I asked, holding up a box of angel hair. "It seems simple enough to make."

"It's low cal, but high carbs. My uncle Fred always said if you want to lose weight, stay off the carbs."

"So what does he suggest?"

"Beef, chicken, eggs."

I'd heard of those high protein, low carb diets. They never sounded all that healthy to me. Yet, if they worked, was that the way to go? We needed to get out of this gridlock. I turned to Darnell. "What would Mr. Griffin do now?" I asked.

"I guess he'd say go back to your goal."

"That's to lose weight. So maybe the all meat diet is a good idea?"

"Well, losing weight is what we put down on the card," he said.

Losing weight was the measurable goal he'd listed, but his vision for himself had been much more than that. "Right, you also want to be healthy and fit. So maybe just eating meat isn't the way to go?"

Darnell shrugged.

"What about vegetables?" I asked.

"What, like broccoli? It's also high carb, isn't it?"

"I have no idea. And I haven't the slightest clue how to cook it."

So we wandered around the supermarket, which felt bigger and more daunting the more time we spent. We needed help. "You know what else Mr. Griffin would say? Turn to your Mastermind Group."

"Christy?" Darnell asked.

"Why not? She's thin and an athlete."

"Plus she's a girl, so she probably knows how to cook," Darnell gave voice to what I'd also been thinking but hadn't wanted to say.

I tried her cell phone. Christy laughed when I told her why we'd called. "Happy to help. You guys have both been there for me. I'm just leaving swim practice now. I'll come meet you."

When she arrived, Christy took one look at our cart and balked. "You're not expecting to lose weight on this stuff, are you?"

Darnell explained about his mom and her shopping list. "We really don't know what to buy for dinner."

"Or how to cook it," I added.

"I want to get something low calorie," Darnell said, "but my uncle says that carbs are bad for losing weight, and we think too much meat sounds unhealthy. So we just froze."

Christy squeezed in her cheeks to keep herself from breaking into giggles. "If you want to go with one of those fad diets, you're on your own. All I can tell you is that my family eats tons of carbs. My mom cooks just like her mom and her mom before that. And we're definitely *not* fat."

"Where's your mom from, anyway?" Darnell asked. "Mexico?"

Christy rolled her eyes. "Not everyone who speaks Spanish is from Mexico, you *gringo!*"

"I'm not a gringo. I'm black, in case you hadn't noticed."

"You don't have to be white to be a gringo, Darnell. You're just a black gringo."

"So where are you from?" Darnell asked,

"Colombia. We moved here when I was three."

"And what do you *eat*?"

"Food, Black Gringo. Real food. Rice and beans and potatoes and corn. We love avocado, mango, salads, and berries."

Christy grabbed an empty shopping cart and led us around the supermarket. We practically had to run to keep up as she piled in black beans, rice, yucca (whatever that was), and dozens of other vegetables.

"Kelvin, grab a plantain." She pointed down a vegetable aisle.

The plantains looked like giant bananas and came in two equally unappetizing varieties, green and hard, or a soft yellowish-brown with black splotches.

I must have stood debating which ones to get for some time, since Christy came up behind me and chose a green one.

"Good choice," I said. "I'll take unripe over rotten any day."

"White Gringo, this is how they're supposed to look. The brown ones are sweet, the green ones savory. And before you make another gringo remark, you eat them cooked, not raw."

She stormed off, but I caught her grinning to herself. Far from being upset, she was thoroughly enjoying bossing us around.

By the time we checked out, we had two full shopping carts worth of food, and the price at the register was astronomical. Yet, the items Christy picked out came in at a tiny fraction of the cost of what we bought for Darnell's mom.

When we reached Darnell's, Christy had us put all the groceries away and clear the countertops before we began. "I can't work in chaos," she said. Cooking brought out her Latin side. She pulled up a Carlos Vives album on her phone and swayed her hips in rhythm as she set the rice to cook, adding some spice that turned it orange. It took all Darnell's focus to stick to his assigned tasks rather than watch Christy at work.

Darnell chopped onions, which got him all teary-eyed, and I peeled and cut the plantain into chunks, but neither of us performed to Christy's standards. "Didn't anyone ever teach you Gringos how to use a knife?" She didn't wait for an answer. "First off, get rid of these puny little things. Haven't you got a chef's knife?"

"What's a chef's knife?" Darnell asked.

Christy groaned. "Just get me the biggest knife you have."

Darnell pulled out a monstrous knife that looked brand new. Christy took one look at it and said, "oh good, you do have a chef's knife. Now pay attention." She took Darnell's cutting board and put the tip of the knife near one edge, leaving the back near the pile of onions. "Now, see where the knife is curved? That's the pivot. Place your left hand there, and rock the knife back and forth." Her right hand rose and fell like lightning, leaving the onion diced into a hundred tiny pieces. She lifted the cutting board over a pot and, with a flick of her wrist, pushed the onions in with the back of the knife. Christy handed me the knife, "Now you try it with the plantains."

I tried to duplicate her motions with little success, though, awkward as I was, I still cut up the plantain far faster than I had with my 'puny' knife. When I finished, she pushed the chunks into the pot with the black beans (we used canned, even though Christy said you should *always* buy dried beans and soak them overnight. She acted like a cappuccino lover forced to drink instant coffee). She sprinkled spices into the pot and brought it to a boil.

Darnell looked around at all we were preparing. "Wait, don't we need a protein?"

Christy smacked him on the forehead. "Beans and rice have tons of protein. You don't know anything about food, do you?"

Darnell's shoulders rose to his ears.

"It's time you got yourself an education, Darnell." She used his real name rather than calling him Black Gringo—Christy was no longer joking around. She looked him square in the eyes. "How else are you going to lose weight while staying healthy?"

"You're right." Darnell nodded. "Smarter, not harder."

"Smarter, not harder."

"I guess getting an education should be the first step on my card. I'm just not sure where to start."

"I'm going to call my mom and tell her I'm staying for dinner," I said. "It smells like Colombian food might not taste so bad after all. Then what do you say we all sit down and brainstorm ways you can learn what you need to know?"

"Sounds good," Darnell said.

"Christy?"

"I'm in, Gringos."

* * *

The Sunday after Christmas started out clear, then snow started falling in late afternoon and didn't stop.

By the time I woke on Monday, December 28, we had eighteen inches of new snow, and guess who was assigned to go clear the driveway so Dad could get out?

I bundled up against the cold, which kept me snug for the first few minutes on the snow blower, but soon enough I was wiping sweat off my forehead.

After about twenty minutes, I'd made minimal progress on the driveway and had already pulled off my jacket to keep from overheating. I turned off the plow for a quick break—the noise of that thing is enough to set you on edge—and I heard a honk. A truck pushed through the slushy streets, flashing its lights.

Jarod pulled up in his pickup, now outfitted with the snowplow on front. "Get out of the way," he told me.

I hauled the snow blower back to the safety of the garage. Jarod lowered his plow and drove right up the driveway, pushing a mountain of snow off to the side. It took him three passes—and no more than five minutes—to clear the entire driveway.

"Thanks," I said.

"Hey, I owe you." Jarod shook my hand. "You won't believe what's going on."

Before he could tell me, my neighbor from across the street opened her front door and came out with a jacket pulled on over her robe. She waved, and I waved back, a little confused, until I realized she wasn't waving at me; she was frantically trying to get Jarod's attention. He signaled to her that he would be over in a minute, then said, "There's another one. It's been like this all morning."

"How many have you done?"

"I've lost count. Hey, why don't you grab your jacket and come with me? I could use the help. I'll give you $20 an hour."

"I can't drive your truck."

"You won't need to. I'll do all of the driving."

I had nothing else to do, and Jarod had already saved me an hour's worth of work on the driveway. I ran into the house, told my father that the driveway was all clear, grabbed a bagel from the breadbox, and was back out by the time Jarod had finished the neighbor's driveway.

She handed him $40 and said, "Are you sure you can't do the walks?"

"The driveways have to take priority for now, but once the snow stops and the driveways are all clear, I'd be happy to come back and do the walks for you. Here, take my number and call me the day after the snow stops."

When we got back into the truck, Jarod said, "Dealing with her took me almost as long as plowing the drive. From now on, that's your job. That, and answering my phone."

"Who will be calling?"

"I honestly have no idea who most of them are or how they got my number."

The phone rang, and I stared at it—Jarod hadn't told me what to say.

"Just put it on speaker for now," he said, and then called out, "Hi, Dr. McCauley."

"Jarod, I heard you've gotten yourself a plow."

"That's right, how can I help you?"

"Any chance you can come by and do my parking lot?"

"Absolutely. You have what, 12 spaces?"

"18."

"That's not a problem. It'll run $200 if you're interested."

"That much?"

"I can do it for $100 tomorrow if the snow stops. But today it's all emergencies."

Dr. McCauley hesitated, then said, "all right."

"Wonderful. I should be in your part of town early this afternoon." Jarod shot me a wink, clearly thinking back to the advice Bill had given him. I knew the location, which was less than two miles away.

There was silence on the line. Finally, Dr. McCauley said, "I'll make it $300 if you can come right now."

Jarod shot me a huge grin. "On my way."

Before we finished Dr. McCauley's parking lot, two adjoining business managers came over and asked us to do theirs. The snow didn't stop falling until 3 pm, and we didn't stop plowing until nearly 10 pm. The phone hardly stopped ringing all day, and by the time Jarod dropped me off at home, I'd left him with a list of bookings for the following day. About half of them were driveways or parking lots, the rest were walkways that he hadn't gotten to today.

I made a couple of hundred dollars for a day of light work. But my earnings were nothing next to Jarod's. He hit his entire monthly earning goal and managed to cover most of the cost of his new plow all in one day.

* * *

I babysat Megan again on New Year's Eve while our parents went out with friends. "You seem different," she said to me.

"Different from who?" I asked as I stirred a bowl of brownie batter.

"From how you used to be." She looked into the bowl and winced. "Those are going to be totally disgusting by the way."

"Darnell told me about the recipe. He said he tried it last week and it turned out pretty good."

"Brownies out of black beans? That sounds so nasty."

"I know. Can I let you in on a secret?"

Megan leaned in. "What's that?"

"I wanted to try it because Darnell said they were good. But I also bought a junky chocolate chip cookie mix in case these turn out as revolting as they sound."

Megan laughed. "How come you changed so much?"

"Oh come on, I haven't changed that much."

"You have. You barely talked to me at all before."

"Nor you to me," I said. "Baking dessert tonight was your idea."

"I guess, but you're so much more approachable now."

A month ago, if anyone asked, I would have said that Megan preferred to be on her own. Had she just felt rejected by me?

"So what changed?"

"If I tell you, do you promise not to laugh?"

She agreed, but within a minute she'd broken her promise. Yet, rather than getting upset, I found myself laughing along with her.

"Generosity Man?"

"Oh yes, I've even got a spandex outfit I put on when I read it. Want to see it?"

She laughed and said yes. I ran upstairs, but of course, I had no spandex outfit. Instead, I threw on a pair of green pajamas and, taking a page from Darnell's book, used tape to put a giant 'G' on my chest.

Megan cracked up when she saw me. "These brownies are going to be so disgusting. Why don't we just make the cookies now?"

I agreed. While she mixed in the fluorescent yellow 'flavor pack,' I said to her, "Would you want to try the notecards? I can help you create your own set."

Megan shrugged. "That's OK."

I didn't push. The desire had to come from her.

We ate our desserts while watching the countdown to the New Year. Shockingly, we liked the brownies more than the cookies. We ate a chocolate chip apiece for each of the final ten seconds. 10, 9, 8, 7, 6, 5, 4, 3, 2, 1.

"Happy New Year!" Megan leaned over and planted a kiss on my cheek.

"Happy New Year, Megan." I hugged her. "Now what do you say you get ready for bed?"

"Fine…" She rolled her eyes, then shot me a grin and headed upstairs.

Once I'd finished the dishes, I went to my room. I knew that Megan was struggling socially, and though she wasn't ready to make a notecard, that didn't mean there was no way I could help her. While I normally emailed if I had anything to write her about, this time I pulled out a piece of stationary and a good pen. I wrote:

Dear Megan,

I had such a great time spending New Year's Eve with you. You are funny, interesting, intelligent, and sensitive. I know that not all of your friends can see the beauty in you, but I want you to know that I do, and if you're able to see it as well, then I'm sure it will not be long until others take notice.

Love,
Kelvin

I slipped the letter under her door and returned to my room. I'd had the best New Year's of my life, but now that I was no longer occupied with my sister, I found my mind wandering back to my classmates and their New Year's parties.

Had I told my parents that I wanted to go to one of the parties, they could have easily gotten a babysitter. Yet, the truth was that I knew I wouldn't be so welcome. Even if they had let me in, I probably would have just sat in a corner on my own, just like Jarod predicted.

I thought over Mr. Griffin's question: *what would I be willing to do to fit in?* If smoking a cigarette would make it easier to be accepted by others, would I do it? What about drugs? At what point would I back out? Drinking and driving?

Mr. Griffin had called drinking and driving an example of the wrong end of Asymmetrical Risk/Reward, with high risk and little reward. But sitting alone in my room at 1 am on New Year's Eve, I found myself falling back into all too familiar patterns of thought and wondered, was the reward really so low? I must be pretty close to the oldest person in the high school to never have a relationship. If I could finally have a girlfriend, wouldn't that be a pretty amazing reward?

Of course, that was just the upside of fitting in. That did nothing to diminish the risk side of the equation. Just thinking of drunk driving brought up thoughts of Christy's coach. A mother of a nine-year-old. Struck down.

Funny how the reward side of the equation would be all mine, but the risk gets spread around. Christy's coach got no benefit from the alcohol. She was just driving home to be with her family. She died, but I heard the drunk driver survived. As my eyes grew drowsy, I found myself wondering what benefit he'd gotten from drinking. Was he also doing it to fit in? Or was it an escape?

Drunk driving. Fitting in. Christy's coach. The words floated around as I drifted closer to sleep.

Christy. Drunk driving.

Somehow, at 1:15 am on New Year's Eve, those ideas fused in my mind. Just thinking of drunk driving, the image that came to my mind was Christy's face.

Not her coach. I'd never seen her coach. Never made it to a swim meet.

Christy. Drunk driving.

Drunk driving. Christy.

And then, as if some cosmic hand was behind the whole thing, my cell phone rang, slapping me fully awake.

I sat up and looked at the number.

It was Jarod. *Why would he be calling me now?* I looked out the window—there was no snow. "What's up, Jarod?"

And then he told me the news.

Chapter Eleven

Rubberwoman

Christy showed up at Derek's funeral in a wheelchair. I wouldn't have recognized her if it weren't for Mrs. Mendez pushing her into the church. Christy's face was swollen and bruised, and her long, black hair had been shaved back on one side to be replaced with stitches and bandages. Her broken leg lay straight out in front of her. Apparently, the doctors hadn't wanted to release her but gave in when she insisted on attending the funeral.

The pastor talked about what a tragedy it was to lose someone so young, with so much life ahead of him. But no matter what my notecard said about sensitivity, I shed no tears for Derek. He'd been a bully in school and hazed the incoming freshmen as though it were his duty, yet his last act had been by far his worst. The only good thing I could say about him was that he'd only managed to kill himself, though one of the injured from the other car was still in critical condition.

School had been canceled for the day, yet I wouldn't have come to the funeral if it hadn't been for Christy. Not that I was feeling too sympathetic toward her either. She bawled her eyes out; whether it was for Derek's loss or her own injuries, I couldn't say.

How could she have been so stupid?

It was bad enough hanging out with a jerk like Derek to begin with, but to get into his car when he'd been drinking? After what happened to her coach?

Derek's mother spoke about what a kindhearted and enthusiastic boy he'd been. It took all my willpower not to groan in disgust as I stomped out the back of the church.

* * *

The next day only Darnell and I showed up to math class. Mr. Griffin told us we wouldn't speak about Christy, not without her present.

I had no interest in speaking about sensitivity, generosity, or any of those other traits today, so when Mr. Griffin asked for updates, I deferred to Darnell. If he was upset about Christy's accident, he hid it better than I did, for he cheerfully went on about the progress he'd made. He'd dropped five pounds since Christmas by spending around two hours a day on his treadmill while watching documentaries and YouTube videos on cooking and nutrition.

Of course, it had been Christy's cooking and her suggestion to get himself an education that led him down this path. She ought to have been there to hear the impact of her feedback and offer suggestions for how he could go farther. And then we could help her figure out how to get her swim team to the state championship. Instead, she was lying bruised and broken, her swim season lost.

I was still thinking about Christy on my way home from school when Jarod's truck pulled up. "Get in, I'll give you a ride."

I climbed into the cab. "Where were you today?"

"Visiting Christy."

"You ditched school to go see her?"

"Yeah. She's home now, just lying in her room all day. She's got plenty of people coming by after school, but both her parents work, and she could use the company during the day. I don't want to miss too many days in a row, though. You want to take tomorrow?"

"Me? Why not one of her friends?"

Jarod groaned. "This crap again? Kelvin, you are her friend."

We both knew that wasn't true. Sure, I'd done her a favor with the swim team video, and she'd paid me back by helping Darnell and I cook, but that was about it. "Trust me, she'd prefer someone else."

"Actually, I think I'll trust *Christy*. I asked her who she wanted to come tomorrow, and she chose you."

"Why?"

"Why not?"

"Cause I..."

"Cause you're not Mr. Cool? Come on, Kelvin, grow up. Think about what Christy's just been through."

The initial shock wore off, and it all made sense. I was the one who always gave without looking for anything in return. Even when I asked Christy for help, it wasn't for me, it was for Darnell. Visiting her would mean ditching school, something I never did, but I couldn't refuse, not to someone in her condition. "Fine, I'll go."

"I'll text you her address. Be there by eight in the morning so her mom can let you in before she goes to work."

* * *

Mrs. Mendez opened the door immediately after I knocked. All teary-eyed, she wrapped me in a tight hug and said, "Gracias divino, gracias." She pointed me toward Christy's bedroom, then slipped past me to get into her car. The house was barely a quarter the size of my own, colorfully decorated, and immaculately clean. I knocked on Christy's door, and she called out, "Who is it?"

"The White Gringo."

"Come on in, Kelvin."

I couldn't remember the last time I entered a girl's bedroom, not counting my sister's. I was expecting a lot more pink. Also absent was any sign of stuffed animals or lace. Instead, I saw turquoise walls adorned with posters of the US Swim team, Shakira, and a curly-haired Latin singer the poster announced was Carlos Vives.

Christy lay in her bed looking even worse than she had at the funeral—her many bruises having turned a greenish-purple. "So glad you're here," she said. "You're just in time for my sponge bath."

"Uhhh…" was all I managed to say.

"Oh, sit down, I'm just kidding. Man, you blush easily."

I plopped down on a green pouf on the floor and realized I was going to be here all day yet didn't know what to say for even the first minute. "So… how are you feeling?"

"Never been better."

I had taken Christy's joke about the sponge bath as an indication she was in high spirits, but I'd misread her completely.

"What did our venerable teacher say about me and the accident?"

"He said we shouldn't talk about you without you in the room."

"I bet he thinks I screwed up. I did, didn't I?"

That was an understatement. But how could I say that?

"Come on, Kelvin. Say something."

I started untying my laces, mainly to buy time to think of a response. Yet, by the time my shoes were off, I'd gotten no further. She no longer wore that smile that welcomed me into the room. Her eyes were bloodshot and sagging, her chin shaking ever so slightly. "I don't know what to say."

"You're disappointed in me...?"

That wasn't what I wanted to communicate, but I couldn't deny it. "Look, it wasn't..." I froze. It wasn't what? Wasn't her fault? I didn't believe that. She knew better. I was here to be on her side, to be sympathetic. But I didn't feel sympathetic.

"Say something, Kelvin."

"I dunno..."

She stared right at me, her expression almost begging. "I'd rather you attack me than sit there and say nothing." Her voice was sharper this time. Was she looking to pick a fight?

But how can you fight an invalid?

"Come on, Kelvin, you're not just gonna sit there like a doofus all day, are you?"

I took the bait. "How could you do this?" I shot up to my feet, unable to contain myself. I couldn't bring myself to look at her, so I just paced before her bed. "You had everything. And you gave it away for...for what?"

"I had *everything*?" She pushed herself higher on the bed. "What *everything* did I have, Kelvin?"

"What? Are you kidding? You were smart, popular, athletic." I almost added beautiful, but that felt like crossing a line.

"No, Kelvin, you're the one who has everything. You're the one who's smart. You're the one who has the fancy computers, the video camera, the parents who would jump to get you a tutor the minute you struggle with anything, who will pay for you to go to any college of your choice. My parents came to this country speaking no English, and the best jobs they could get were as a janitor and a housekeeper. I work my ass off to get the grades I do, and I get no help from anyone.

"No one in my family has ever gone to college. If I want to go, I have to pay for it myself. You act like I'm some natural born athlete. I worked twice as hard as any other girl on that swim team because I knew an athletic scholarship was my one chance for a free college education."

"And you gave all that away to get a ride home from some drunk jerk?"

"Have some respect for the dead!"

Respect? She must be kidding me. "He called me far worse when he was alive."

"No doubt. And I'm sure you called him plenty of awful things behind his back. And despite all of that, had he ever wanted to include you, you would have jumped at the chance to be his friend."

"But he never did include me."

"No, he didn't. But you know why he included me? You know why everyone includes me?"

"Yes, because you're beautiful and fun and—."

"Ha! There are girls far more beautiful than me in our school who you've never even noticed because they're not popular. You know why I have friends, and these girls don't? Because I work as hard on my friendships as I do on my schoolwork and athletics. If I want to be friends with someone, I don't wait for them to come to me, I reach out to *them*."

"So where are all of these friends now? Why am I here while they're all in school?"

"Why? Because I reached out to you, Kelvin." Christy stopped screaming, and her head sank. "Because I need help. And I asked myself, of all my friends, who could best help me in this moment? I thought of you."

Oh. My voice quieted to match hers. "Why me?"

"Because these past two months, I've seen you struggling with yourself like I'm struggling now. I've screwed up in the biggest way, and I'm disgusted with myself for it. I can't even look at myself in the mirror." A tear welled up in her eye until it spilled over and ran down her cheek. "I'm not going to take on massive debt to go to college—I won't mortgage my future that way. Swimming was my one chance, and now I've blown it." She wiped her eyes with her fingers then looked up at me again. "As much as you might hate me right now, it's nothing compared to how much I hate myself."

"I don't hate you, Christy. I just got angry."

"Not nearly as angry as I've been. And I don't want to be, Kelvin. I don't want to hate myself. And I don't want to go on the antidepressants half my friends are on. But I don't know another way to get myself out of it."

"Half your friends are on antidepressants?"

"That comes as a surprise to you?"

"Well, yeah. Like who?"

"Like Lindsay, Simon, Haley, Monica, Jessy—."

"Monica Grey?"

"You're surprised? You think she wakes up that perky? Monica's taken medication since eighth grade, and she's been hospitalized twice for bulimia."

"But—."

"Let me guess. You think because she's pretty, she has no reason to be depressed?"

I fell back into the pouf. "I guess I did."

"It's time to come out of your bubble, Kelvin." Christy settled into her pillow.

I was feeling more and more like a schmuck for coming into her house and yelling at her. "I guess you're right. But let's remember that *you* called *me* here. How do you think I can help you?"

"You're not as shy as you were a few months ago. Not just around us, but in general."

"Didn't realize you were watching so closely."

"You're not as unique or mysterious as you think. Plus, this is the 'thing' you're working on with your notecards. Just like I care how much Darnell weighs and how much Jarod makes, I've been watching your progress." Christy raised an eyebrow on the uninjured side of her face. "You're starting to like yourself more, aren't you?"

I hadn't thought of it in those terms, but when she said it, I knew it was true. "Yes."

"That's what I need, now. I want to like myself again. I need to forgive myself."

I wanted to forgive her too. I didn't want to be holding so much anger and frustration towards...towards my friend.

Christy said, "How much of the change do you attribute to your Identity card?"

"That's what started it."

"You think it can help me?"

"Let's find out. You have a hand mirror?"

"Oh, no, no, no! I've got a blank notecard on my desk. Let's start there."

I understood the hesitancy to get in front of the mirror, but that's precisely why we needed it. "Mirror," I said.

"We'll get there, but not yet."

I learned from Mr. Griffin that there was a time to be gentle and a time to be strong. "You tell me where the mirror is, or I'm leaving."

Christy crossed her arms. "Fine. My mom's got one in the bathroom."

The house just had one bathroom, yet there were enough perfumes, colognes, and hair care products to supply a small department store, all lined up in perfect rows. The hand mirror hung on a hook next to the medicine cabinet, no doubt to make sure the Mendez family appeared well groomed from all angles.

I brought it back to Christy and said, "You know what to do."

Christy's eyes teared, and she turned her head away after barely a glance. Of course, I'd reacted much the same way the first time I stood before the mirror, without the excuse of a car accident.

Still, this was not the time to coddle: "Look."

Christy forced herself to gaze into the mirror, then drew away.

"Come on, your face is not that bad."

"You shut your mouth before I give you one to match, Gringo. I'm not turning away from my face but from my eyes."

I remembered looking into my eyes that first time—they reflected my disappointment back at me. "That was the hardest for me, too."

"How'd you get over it?"

"I just did it, over and over again. No other way."

Christy inched her head back towards the mirror. "I can't."

"Don't be such a wuss. Just...I dunno...Imagine this is a swim meet and you're up against the top team in the state. Muster whatever you've got. It's just a mirror."

With her eyes still pinched, she turned and finally faced the mirror. "Fine. Happy?"

"Now, 'I love you, Christy.'"

"Love you too, Kelvin."

"You think jokes will make this easier, but they won't. Trust me, I've tried that many times. They only make it harder to be real with yourself. Say it."

"I love you, Christy." She collapsed into tears. "But I don't. I don't love myself. I worked so hard for years, and then ruined everything."

A memory from earlier in the year came rushing back. "Remember what Mr. Griffin told Darnell after Thanksgiving? 'Certain moments define a lifetime.' Maybe this is your moment. Right now, you're going to decide whether you're going to be stronger than this, or it's going to be stronger than you."

"What if it *is* stronger than me?"

I didn't have an easy answer. I knew that somewhere inside, Christy had tremendous strength and courage. But it wasn't going to be sweet-talked out of her. She loved Coach Dana but chose Coach Sue. To help Christy, I had to be tough like Sue. "Then you might as well give up now. I'll go put the mirror away." I stood up and reached out for the mirror.

Christy took a deep breath. "No. Wait, I'll do it. Just be nice, OK?"

"I can coddle you or I can help you, but I don't think I can do both. Choose."

"Help me. Please, help me."

I sat back down "You know what to do."

Christy held her gaze. She writhed, but no longer turned away. "I love you, Christy."

"I am resilient," I said.

"I am resilient."

"Now give me three examples of your resilience."

"OK, let me think. I didn't drop the swim team when we lost our coach. Um...I studied my butt off in chemistry after I failed our first exam, and still came out of that class with a B+..."

"Great, just one more."

"I called you because I didn't want to give into my guilt. I wanted to be stronger than this."

"That's what I'm talking about." I gave Christy a high-five. "Now for the last step. Say, 'In fact, I'm so resilient, I am....'"

"In fact," she repeated, "I am so resilient, I am...what?"

"Rubberwoman," I said.

"Rubberwoman?"

"Sure, Rubberwoman. You always bounce back."

"Kelvin..." Christy rolled her eyes and cracked a smile, "that is so corny."

"The cornier the better. But if you can think of anything you like more, go for it."

"In fact, I am so resilient, I am Rubberwoman." Christy laughed. Good, she was starting to enjoy this.

"I am dependable," I said.

"I am dependable." Without waiting for me, she said, "OK, three examples. My mom knows she can always count on me around the house. And...the team voted me captain cause they know I'll be there for them. Also, when my friends need someone to talk to, they know I'll listen."

"Good, in fact—."

"Shut up, Kelvin before you give me some other lame name." Christy took a deep breath. "In fact, I'm so dependable, they call me The Rock."

"Amazing, Rock. What should we do next?"

"I don't know. How do I decide?"

"Think of traits you so badly need to believe you have, but the accident totally trashed."

Christy thought for a moment, then said, "I am an inspiration."

"Great, gimme reasons."

"Well, I inspired Darnell to want to cook *real* food."

"Totally. What else?"

"Our whole coach search inspired the team to work much harder this year."

"Plus got our whole school behind you guys."

"Not to mention all those coaches who offered us help and advice—and, of course, free coaching." Christy examined herself in the mirror as if for the first time. Her expression turned pensive. "I think I've inspired my parents. They came to America to make a better life for us, and I think they've been blown away by all I've done."

"Great. That's three."

"In fact," Christy said, "I am so inspiring, I'm....Who's inspiring?"

"I don't know, Gandhi?"

"I'm not going to be *Gandhi*, give me a break."

I scanned the room and saw fireworks above the Shakira poster. "How about a shooting star?"

"Good. I'm so inspiring, I'm a Shooting Star." She made glamorous faces into the mirror—well, as glamorous as a crash test dummy can get.

The light in Christy's eyes had returned. "Okay. One last statement. I am beautiful." She studied her stitches in the mirror. "In fact, I'm so beautiful, I look just like the Bride of Frankenstein."

I grabbed the mirror from her hand and took a hard look at myself. Suddenly, I liked what I saw. "I am wise," I said, and at the moment, I felt it. "I am so wise, I am a fortune cookie."

Christy grabbed back the mirror and held it out so that we could both see ourselves in it. "We are friends," she said. "In fact, we're such good friends, we're like..."

"Batman and Rubberwoman."

Chapter Twelve

The Lawn Ranger

"So, Jarod, how's your business going?" Mr. Griffin asked.

"I'm doing better and better. But I wouldn't really call what I have a business yet." Jarod's hands turned up. "I'm still just a guy pushing a lawnmower."

"I see. And what defines a business?"

"Well, take Bill, for example. He's got a business. His trucks are all the same color, and they've got his logo on them. He has proper receipts. He's got a staff with t-shirts that say *Greenscapes Lawncare: We're Here to Serve*. He's even got a secretary taking all his calls."

"Without the t-shirts would it still be a business?"

"Sure."

"What if Bill's trucks didn't have his logo?"

"I guess. But—"

"But what?"

"It feels different, what Bill's got. I don't think of myself that way."

"Precisely. Because once you get past all of the t-shirts, logos and other minor details, you'll find that only one thing separates you from a legitimate business."

"What's that?"

"Mindset. Businesses take themselves seriously, and you don't."

"I take myself seriously."

"Do you? Why don't you try, just for a day, to think of yourself not as a guy who pushes a mower, but as the head of a landscaping business? See how that affects you."

* * *

Jarod bounced into class the next morning. "What do you all think?" He held up a piece of paper for all to see.

"The Lawn Ranger?" Darnell asked.

"Glad to see you made an Identity Card," I said. "That's a great nickname."

"It's not a nickname, it's the new name of my business."

"Why not Jarod's Landscaping or something like that?" Darnell asked.

"At first I wanted to call it Jarod's Lawn Care, but I thought about Bill and how he has this huge staff of guys not named 'Bill.' This name allows the business to grow into something bigger than me."

"Where'd the name come from?" Darnell asked.

"Believe it or not, it's what my grandfather has called me ever since I started mowing. He's a Lone Ranger buff. I thought it was catchy."

"That's a real shift," Mr. Griffin said.

"I took our conversation yesterday to heart."

"So what now?"

"Well," Jarod pulled out a notecard, "my girlfriend Emily and I made a list last night of all the things that a legit business has that I don't. You were right that none of them, other than taking myself seriously, is a big deal, but that doesn't mean I don't have to get them done. Tops on my list are registering with the state and making a logo. Kelvin, are you up for helping me on the design?"

"Sure," I said.

"But this time I want to pay you. A proper business compensates people for their services."

* * *

"Welcome back, Christy," Mr. Griffin said on Monday morning. Christy hobbled into the room on a pair of crutches. Jarod walked in behind her, carrying her backpack. "How are you feeling?"

"Better the last few days."

"Wonderful." Mr. Griffin sat down on the edge of his desk. "Now that we've got the full Mastermind Group back together, why don't you update us on all that's happened."

Christy shared about the accident and about how depressed she felt afterward. "Then Kelvin told me that my response would be one of those moments that define the rest of my life, just like you told Darnell after Thanksgiving. He helped me turn things around and create an Identity Card. I don't want to fall into depression."

Christy swallowed. "I had nothing else to do with my time, so I've been spending almost two hours a day in front of the mirror reading my card and thinking of examples to back up each statement. I'm surprised at how much it's helped."

"I'm glad to hear it's working so well for you." Mr. Griffin stepped up to her desk. "Now please give us a full update on how your other card is going."

"What other card?"

"Your swimming card, of course."

"Have you seen me? My swimming season is done."

"You still have your swimming card?"

Christy tightened her brow. "Yeah. So?"

"Read it."

Christy pulled out a worn notecard from the bottom of her bag and read:

I intend to captain the girls' swim team to victory in the State Championships on March 8th. To accomplish this ...

"Stop," Mr. Griffin said. "That's enough."

Christy sent him a look that said, 'no kidding,' and shoved the card back in her bag.

"Wait, Christy. Not yet. You still haven't updated us on your progress."

"The progress, Mister Griffin," she said his name slowly, with mock respect, "is that my swimming season is oooooooover. I couldn't beat a tortoise in a race. I have failed!" Christy grabbed either end of the notecard and was about to tear it in half.

"That's strange." Mr. Griffin stepped to the front of the room and leaned into his chair, "I don't recall your card mentioning anything at all about swimming. Read it again."

Christy's eyes narrowed, but she wasn't one to refuse a teacher.

I intend to captain the girls' swim team to victory in the State Championships on March 8th. To accomplish this, I will do the following:

1. Find an amazing coach
2. Inspire the team to fully cooperate with the coach
3. Build up team spirit
4. Recruit school and community support for the team

"Again," Mr. Griffin said, "I don't hear a single step that involves swimming. Do you?"

"The swimming part is *obvious*. You can't win a championship if you don't swim."

"I agree that you can't win a championship if *no one* swims. But even before your accident, the two best swimmers on the team were not even planning on racing."

"Who's that?"

"Coach Sue and Coach Dana, of course. Not everyone needs to swim for the swim team to be successful."

"Look, Mr. Griffin, I know what you want me to say, that I'll push through anyway and captain the team to the championship, even if I can't race. That sounds good and all, but it's just not happening. I know our girls. I know who can do what. And without me racing, we'll still win some meets, but we can't win it all. It's hopeless."

"Hopeless? Remember, that's what you said a couple of months ago. Yet, a few weeks later you'd discovered your hope."

"But I've already done everything I could think of to help the team win."

"Did you? That wasn't my experience."

Christy's fist tightened under her desk. "What was your experience?"

"I saw that you worked like hell to get the team to the point where you thought you had a good chance of winning the championship. Once you thought you were good enough, you became content to ride it out."

Christy's lips trembled. "What more could I have done?"

"I don't know," Mr. Griffin shrugged. "But when was the last time you used your Mastermind Group to brainstorm how you could make your team better?"

Christy's shoulders dropped, and her voice quieted. "I guess it's been over a month now."

"I can't stress enough, Christy, how important it is to see your goal through to the end. Kelvin was right that your response to this accident could define the rest of your life. But it's not enough to just get over this, to bring your life back to being almost as good as it was before. Something positive must come out of this accident."

"What possibly could be *positive* about this?"

"I don't know, but remember, life happens *for* you, not *to* you. Somewhere inside this accident is embedded one of the greatest lessons of your life. If you let the accident hold you back, if you let it demoralize you, you'll likely never discover it."

"So how do I find it?"

"By pushing through to your goal. Besides, keeping your goal might be just the thing you need to accelerate your recovery."

"How can the goal help with recovery?"

"Strong goals pull. They'll pull you out of bed in the morning, pull you through bad days, pull you through distraction. It can even pull you through a disaster as long as the goal is bigger than the disaster. But if you decide that the disaster is bigger than your goal, it can lead you to despair."

Christy turned to us. "Guys, do you agree? Is there anything I can still do to get the team back on track?"

Jarod raised a finger. "It seems to me that the only thing that's changed is that you're down one top-notch swimmer. You think any of the younger girls can step up?"

"And replace me? I don't mean to be arrogant here, but no freakin' way."

"Then what about someone not on the team?" I asked. "Didn't a bunch of girls approach you when that article came out in the local paper?"

"Yeah, four girls asked if they could join, though one of them homeschools, so she's not even eligible."

"But you've never actually seen any of them swim, right?" I said.

"What are you suggesting? New try-outs? You really think there's some star swimmer out there who didn't bother trying out on time?"

"I know it sounds stupid, but what have you got to lose?" I asked.

Christy shrugged. "I guess nothing."

"Who knows," I added, "maybe you could convince that homeschool girl to enroll for the semester."

"Let's see if she can swim first. You have no idea how many girls who try out can barely do a butterfly. Any other ideas?"

"Diet," Darnell said.

"Diet?" Christy chuckled. "These girls aren't exactly fat, Darnell."

"Diet is about a lot more than just losing weight, you know."

"I know that," Christy said, "but when did you learn that?"

"A lot can happen in two weeks. I've learned quite a bit since Christmas."

"So have I," Christy said. "But finish your thought."

"Well, with the right diet, I bet a bunch of these girls could start performing better. But I wasn't thinking about them anyway. I meant for you. I was watching a video the other day about how your diet impacts your recovery time from injury."

"You think a change in what I eat is going to suddenly allow me to come back a month early? Because that's what I'd need to be ready for States."

"I think," Jarod said, "that when you put your mind to something, you're a force to be reckoned with. The Christy I know would have been lifting weights in the hospital if she thought she could come back in time."

"Jarod, you have *any idea* how long it takes to come back from a broken leg?"

"Not really. Do you?"

"The doctor told me I shouldn't expect to walk without a cast for two months."

"Then it's a good thing for you the state eliminated that pool walking event from the championships."

Christy shoved her finger in Jarod's chest. "You got a point, funny guy?"

"I expect swimming puts far less stress on your legs than walking. Do you know how long it'll be before you'll be allowed back in the pool?"

"I assume not until the cast comes off."

"Sounds to me like you don't know," Jarod said. "What can you do now to prepare the rest of your body so that the moment you can use your leg again, you're ready to go?"

Christy thought for a moment. "You know, I really don't know."

"So who does?" Darnell asked. "Is there an expert you can ask?"

Christy chewed on her lip. "Coach Sue might know. Or at least she'd know who to ask." She swallowed hard and added, "I'd better speak to her about that as well as scheduling new try-outs. That's her decision anyway. Darnell, can you help me figure out how to shift my diet?"

A grin brought out the dimples in Darnell's cheeks. "Gladly." It was probably the first time in his life anyone asked him for advice on food.

* * *

"Coach Sue thinks there's a slim chance I can make it back," Christy reported the next day. "Though even if I can, I won't be the same swimmer this year."

"How long until you can get into the pool?" Mr. Griffin asked.

"The doctors planned to replace my cast with a smaller one in about two weeks. Coach Sue told me that if they make the new one waterproof, I'll be able to get into the pool almost immediately. She said swimming anyway puts far less strain on a break than running, so the chances of re-injury are slim."

"What did she say about new try-outs?"

"At first she said no. She said we don't go reforming the team every time someone gets hurt."

"At first?" Mr. Griffin asked.

"She eventually relented when I explained how committed I was to winning the state championships and how guilty I felt about the accident. She doesn't expect anything to come of tryouts, but she told me she'd come to the pool a half hour early today and would check out any girl wanting to join the team.

So I've called all the girls that had been in contact with me earlier. One is no longer interested, but three are coming."

Mr. Griffin smiled. "Let this be a lesson to all of you. When there's a disagreement between two people, who wins?"

"I would have said the one in charge," Jarod said, "but it didn't work out that way this time."

"How about the one that's the loudest?" Darnell said.

"No way," Christy said. "The surest way to lose with Coach Sue is to raise your voice. She won't have anyone challenging her authority."

"In my experience," Mr. Griffin said, "90% of the time the one with the greatest *will* prevails."

"So you think Christy won because she wanted it more?" Jarod asked.

"No. Will and desire are not the same thing, though desire certainly plays a role. Christy had a clear outcome and an iron will. Coach Sue only had a general idea about what she wanted and clearly didn't care all that much if it went her way. Despite being louder and having all the authority, she had little chance."

"One more update," Christy said. "Darnell's been a champ at digging up information. I've already started on his Popeye diet."

"Popeye diet?" Jarod asked.

"That's what I'm calling it," Christy said, "because he's got me eating all this spinach."

"Not just spinach," Darnell said. "But spinach is high in calcium and zinc, both of which are important for injury recovery. Broccoli, cabbage, and kale are also good. She also needs vitamins C, D, and K, as well as protein to rebuild the bones."

"If she needs calcium and protein," Jarod said, "why not just put her on cheeseburgers?"

"She needs foods that are anti-inflammatory." Darnell's temper rose, then calmed down when he saw that Jarod was just messing with him. "Beans are good for protein, and if she adds turmeric they'll be even better."

"Wow, you really know what you're talking about," Jarod said.

"Not really. I didn't know any of this yesterday. I spent a couple of hours last night going through websites that have articles on this stuff. I don't even know what turmeric tastes like."

"Still," Mr. Griffin said, "it sounds like you've been learning quite a bit about food. I imagine that's been helping you move toward your own goal?"

"Yeah." Darnell's voice sounded surprisingly unenthusiastic.

"Something bothering you Darnell?" Mr. Griffin asked. "Are you finding the new diet hard to keep?"

"No, the diet's been great. The more I learn, the more I enjoy cooking. There are a few healthy chefs I'm following on YouTube and, though my dishes don't come out looking anything like theirs, I'm improving, and the food tastes far better than I expected."

"So what's the problem?"

Darnell twisted the cap on and off his pen. "It's my goal."

"Ah, you're not losing weight as fast as you'd like?" Mr. Griffin asked.

"No, that's not it. I'm on pace to easily exceed my goal this month. I just don't feel motivated by it any longer."

"Why not?"

"Well, when I started, I was just sick of being a fat guy. Each day I'd jump on the scale, and if my weight had dropped a pound, I was thrilled. If it climbed, I was devastated."

"And now?"

"Now I'm dragging myself onto the scale, and even when I see my weight drop, I don't care all that much."

"What's changed?" Mr. Griffin asked.

"I guess I'm seeing that if I eat right and get the exercise I need, the weight will take care of itself."

"So what do you find motivating?"

"Believe it or not: *learning*. There is so much about food and health that I didn't know. I mean, I knew my eating was unhealthy—any idiot knows soda and ice cream aren't good for you—but I really couldn't have told you what a healthy diet looked like. I'm enjoying learning about new foods and preparing them. And I love the fact that I can feel the difference. I have more energy and stamina. But reading my card isn't all that motivating."

"It sounds to me like you're ready for a new goal."

"It's OK. I've only got a week to go 'til I hit the deadline on this one. I should make it easily. I'll make myself a new card then."

Mr. Griffin laughed. "Why wait?"

"*Why wait?* Mr. Griffin, you're always telling us the value of seeing our goals through to the end. Jarod spent $200 on Cirque du Soleil tickets and ditched a day of school because you wouldn't let him budge on his goal."

"The show was excellent, by the way," Jarod added. "My girlfriend and I went last week. Not sure I'd spend another $200 to do it again, but I have no regrets."

"See?" Darnell said. "Now you want me to drop my goal with a week to go?"

"Jarod's goal," Mr. Griffin said, "was still meaningful to him. He just wanted to give it up because he didn't think he could make it. That's a time you've got to push through, or else you'll find yourself giving up whenever you face an obstacle. But your goal, Darnell, has lost its juice. In fact, seeing your face when you talk about it, I wonder if the goal is *demotivating* you. What possible purpose is there in holding onto a goal you couldn't care less about reaching?"

"I do want to reach it," Darnell said, "because I want to be a person who sees his goals through to the end."

"Go to any law school and ask the third-year students about their career hopes. You'll be shocked at how many of them have already decided that law is not for them but are sticking out their degree because they think it's important to finish what they begin. Meanwhile, they're racking up a fortune in debt and wasting time they could be spending building something they do want for their lives."

"So you'd have them quit?" Darnell asked.

"Absolutely. I've never understood why quitters get such a bad rap. I'm a huge fan of quitting."

"*You?*" Christy said. "After all the hell you gave me yesterday when I wanted to quit?"

"Again, it all depends on the reason you're quitting. You, Christy, are dying to win the state championship in swimming, you wanted to quit because you thought it was beyond your reach."

"Still do."

"That may be, but my point is that you still *want it*. I know that you're capable of so much more than you realize. My aim is to make you see that as well. So no way I'm going to let you walk away from a goal just because it's hard." Mr. Griffin stepped in front of Darnell's desk and leaned in. "But a goal that you no longer want? That you no longer find motivating? Chuck it. Find your fire. Find your passion. Create a new goal that lights you up and go after that."

"So what should my new goal be?" Darnell asked.

"You tell me. Where are your passions right now?"

"My passions are in learning more about food and how to cook healthy meals."

"So there you go. You need to create a goal around that."

"But I don't see how it fits our structure. Weight was such an easy goal because it's so measurable. How do I write 'learn more about health' into an Outcome Card?"

"You're right, it doesn't fit our normal structure, and it's important that milestones be measurable. However, there's a big difference between lead and lag measures." Mr. Griffin grabbed a new notecard for Darnell. "Go ahead and tear up that old notecard. We're going to replace it with what I call a Continual Growth card."

Darnell's face lit up like a kid before a piñata as he tore his card to shreds. "How do I make a Continual Growth card?"

"Continual Growth cards are almost a hybrid of our Outcome Cards and our Identity Cards. Like the Outcome Cards, they do have a clear objective, but the objective is not measurable, and like the Identity Cards, there's no end date."

"I thought you said it's important that we choose measurable objectives?" Darnell asked.

"It is. But on Continual Growth cards, it's the steps, not the objective, that are measurable. Also, we're going to shift from lag to lead measures. Lag measures tend to be easier to get our heads around, but lead measures can be far more powerful."

"What are lag and lead measures?" Jarod asked.

"A lag measure comes after the work. For instance, if you want to see how much weight you've lost in the last week, you can hop on a scale. The lag measure tells you nothing about the future, just what you've done in the past."

"So a lead measure is a future based measurement?" Jarod asked.

"Precisely."

"Can you give us an example?" Christy asked.

"To get in shape, I'll go for a 5K run every morning at 6 am," Mr. Griffin said. "It tells you exactly what you're going to do, and when you're going to do it."

"So then how will I know when I've met my objective?" Darnell said.

"You never will. That's the idea, it's a card focused on an area where you know you'll want to keep improving indefinitely."

"So I'm going to be stuck with this card for life?" Darnell asked.

"You'll have it as long as it serves you. I've torn up many Continual Growth cards over the years, not because I achieved their objective, but because my priorities changed."

"When we started this whole card business," Jarod said, "you were pretty insistent we have a clear goal with a timeline."

"I was. Continual Growth cards are simpler, which ironically makes them harder to keep to. I always recommend starting with the Outcome cards and adding Continual Growth cards only once the notecards are a part of your life. Darnell, what's your objective?"

"Well, I want to learn more about health and cooking."

"Is that your objective, just to learn?"

"No, I guess not. My objective is to be healthy."

"Better. But 'be healthy' is rather blah language, isn't it? Let's see if we can't spice it up a little. We want to come up with something that will give you an emotional charge."

"Um...Like what?"

"Start by throwing out some words. What are things you want?"

"Health. Energy."

"Mastermind group, help him along."

"How about vibrancy, Darnell?" I said.

"Stamina?" Christy said.

"Yeah, those are good," Darnell said.

"OK, so for a first draft," Mr. Griffin wrote on the board, "let's try:

I intend to continually improve my health, energy, vibrancy, and stamina. To accomplish this, I will:

"Mastermind group, what are things Darnell can do to reach this goal?"

"I know Darnell's been watching food videos while on his treadmill," I said. "It sounds like that's been working."

"And cooking meals," Christy said.

"Correct," Mr. Griffin said, "but remember, on the Continual Growth Cards, the steps have to be measurable."

I chewed on my pen. "So could a step be to watch at least one hour of health videos each day while walking on the treadmill?"

"Precisely, Kelvin. Christy, can you make the same change to your step?"

"Uh, OK. So Darnell could make sure to cook at least one healthy meal per day. Would that work?"

"Don't ask me. Darnell, what do you think?"

"It sounds pretty good."

"Just pretty good? If that's all, then we're not there yet. What do you think we're missing, Darnell?"

"Well, I like the learning, even if it's not just for me. Last night, when I looked up how diet can help recovery from injury, I was fascinated by it, even though I was looking it up for Christy. But the way we have it here, it doesn't support my objective."

"I see what's bothering you," Mr. Griffin said. "Can you see how to fix it?"

"Well if I want to be doing more learning, even if it's not for me, then it seems like the learning itself needs to be in the objective. Right?"

"You know Darnell," Mr. Griffin said, "I do believe you're getting this."

"The same goes for the cooking," Darnell added. "If I wanted to cook just to have healthy foods to eat, I could get by with just making the same things over and over. But I'm having fun experimenting with new ingredients. So I think that should also be in the objective."

"Wonderful. Write it out and read off your new objective."

Darnell bent over his card. "Got it. It now says:

I intend to continually improve my health, energy, vibrancy, and stamina, and to continually increase my knowledge about health and cooking. To accomplish this, I will:

1) Watch at least one hour of health-related videos per day while walking on my treadmill
2) Cook healthy meals at least five times per week
3) Experiment with at least one new ingredient per week

"I want everyone to notice," Mr. Griffin said, "that I used the phrase 'continually grow' when I wrote a draft of the card, and Darnell changed that to 'continually improve' and 'continually increase' on his version of the card. Does anyone see a problem with that?"

I knew Mr. Griffin was meticulous in the language he used for these cards, but I couldn't see the issue. Apparently, no one else could either.

"Good," Mr. Griffin said, "I'm glad no one said anything. For the fact is, there is no problem. Darnell preserved the function of the card while switching to language that spoke to him. Using language that inspires you is key to the effectiveness of the cards. So Darnell, how do you feel about your new card?"

"It's a big improvement over the old one."

* * *

Christy invited me to watch the swim team tryouts since they were my idea. I suspected she just wanted me to see with my own eyes how pathetic the new girls would be. Though she was going along with the steps we suggested, she wasn't particularly optimistic they'd make a difference. I'd had enough experience by now with the notecards to know that was still OK. They were a tool for building momentum and didn't need to create an overnight miracle.

"What kind of girl…" Christy had just gotten her first glimpse of the potential recruits, "shows up for a swim team tryout in a bikini?" She shot me a look that said *this is all your fault*, then hobbled off to join Coach Sue by the side of the pool.

I actually thought the girl in the bikini looked quite good. Until she got in the water. Christy watched her swim all of two ungainly strokes, then flipped me the finger. Bad as she was, at least she wasn't the worst of the girls trying out. The second girl hit the water with such a splash that even I got wet in the bleachers. This time, Christy just laughed in my direction.

The third girl sat reading a book, not even watching the first two trials. She was the only one of the three who bothered to wear a swim cap, though admittedly it looked pretty stupid with her reading glasses over it. Coach Sue called out to her, "Amanda, it's your turn. *Amanda!*"

The second call got her attention. She removed her glasses, lay them on her book, and stepped to the edge of the pool. Coach Sue held out her stopwatch. "On your marks, get set, Go!"

Now I'd never actually been to a swim meet, so I didn't have much to compare her to, but *damn*, that girl was *fast!* Christy and Coach Sue exchanged a look. When Amanda reached the end of the pool, she turned awkwardly, not like the flip-turns I'd seen Christy do the first time I'd attended practice. Coach Sue kept peeking down at her stopwatch and slammed down the hammer the moment Amanda hit the edge of the pool. She held it out for Christy to see and the two of them spoke in hushed tones.

Amanda pulled herself out of the pool, and I slipped down from my place on the bleachers to listen in. Coach Sue said, "Nice job," and strode away to deal with the girls arriving for practice.

Amanda toweled off and approached Christy. "Your coach didn't seem so pleased with me."

"She had mixed reactions and said it's my call as captain."

"Isn't that normally the coach's decision?"

"Normally. But I'm the one who needs replacing, and I wanted the tryout, so she's passing the decision off to me."

Amanda bounced on her tiptoes. "So...am I on the team?"

"Why don't you shower and get dressed, and we'll discuss it."

Amanda shrugged and headed toward the locker room. Once she was out of earshot, I said, "You're going to take her, right?"

"I'm not sure."

"No? I don't know much about swimming, but she seemed good. How was her time?"

"I've swum as fast as she did that first lap twice before, but never in practice."

"She's faster than *you*?"

"Only on that first lap. Her turn was awful. She's clearly never been coached."

"But with a little coaching, she can be good?"

"Yeah. But Coach Sue already worked with the team on turns early in the year. She's not interested in changing her coaching for one girl. She can give me a little bit of Coach Dana's time to work with Amanda, but mainly, if I want her to get good, I'd have to help her myself."

"Are you able to do that? Are you good enough to help her out?"

"Yeah, I could. Especially with Dana's help."

"So what's the question?"

"She's the homeschooler."

"So she can only swim if we convince her to enroll in school?"

"Right."

"Well, maybe she's prepared to. After all, she got in touch with you, so she wants to be part of this. And she'd only have to be in school for a couple of months anyway."

"Yeah, maybe."

Something didn't add up. Christy thought the team had a great chance at winning the state championship before her accident. Then, with her injury, she thought there was little chance. Now she found someone who could be even faster than her and get the team back on track. Why was she so lukewarm? "What's going on with you, Christy?"

"I don't know." She looked down into the water. Was she sad? Disappointed? I got a dark feeling in my gut. "You don't want her to succeed, do you?"

Her head jumped up. "Of course I do."

"There's a part of you that's hoping she doesn't enroll, isn't there?"

"She'll be good for the team. Of course, I want her."

"What's your goal, Christy?"

"You know what my goal is."

"Tell me again."

"My goal is to win the state championship." There was no life in her voice.

"Louder. What's your goal?"

Christy rolled her eyes. "My goal is to win the state championship," she mumbled.

"I can barely hear you. Come on, one more time. What's your goal, Christy?"

Her eyes shot up to mine, and she almost yelled, "My goal was to get a swimming scholarship, damn it!"

"But your card says—."

"I know what my card says, and I want to win. I do. I want to do it in memory of my coach, and I want to do it for the team. But I'd also wanted to do it for *me*. If we won the championship, as captain and anchor, I'd be set for a swimming scholarship, and I'd be able to afford to go to college.

"Once I got hurt, all that went out the window. College coaches only have so many scholarships to give out, and if they give one to someone who's suffered a major injury, that's taking a big risk. Even if a coach was impressed by me, she'd still wonder if I could make a full recovery. You guys helped me see that coming back really is possible. That means my best chance for getting my scholarship is to put every ounce of energy I've got into rehabbing myself. If I can make it back this year, I've still got a shot. I don't think I can do that and be Amanda's coach at the same time."

I didn't know what to say. Amanda came out of the locker room. Her hair was pulled back tight behind her, and she wore baggy overalls atop a mismatched flannel shirt.

Christy braced herself, then said, "You swam really well, Amanda. We'd definitely take you on the team if you were eligible. Unfortunately, you don't actually go to our school. So unless you're planning on enrolling, there's not much we can do."

If I wanted to convince Amanda to enroll, I would have talked to her about the amazing things the team was doing, made her feel like being part of such an incredible team was worth the sacrifice of a couple of months of school. The fact that Christy didn't even meet Amanda's eyes as she spoke told me she'd made her decision to put her scholarship ahead of the team.

"Oh, that's not a problem," Amanda said. "I'm already eligible."

"But you don't go to the school," Christy said.

"That doesn't matter. The state's Equal Access law gives homeschoolers the right to participate in school sports. You don't think I would have contacted you if I wasn't eligible, do you?"

Now Christy was stuck. She'd already told Amanda she could join. Her shoulders sagged as she extended a hand and forced a big smile. "Welcome to the team."

Chapter Thirteen

Tuition

Christy was a mess the next day. Her eyes were bloodshot, and she groaned with each hobble on her crutches. When Mr. Griffin asked her what was going on, she came right out and said, "I tried to sabotage the team." Tears rained down her face.

She launched into the entire story of the tryout, including some details that I hadn't even known, such as Coach Sue pointing out the flaws in Amanda's stroke, saying that she could be even faster with the right coaching.

"I tried reading my Identity Card since then," she said, "but I can't even look myself in the eye."

"Guilt over an issue is often far worse than the issue itself," Mr. Griffin said.

"How is that?" Christy asked.

"Look at yourself now," Mr. Griffin said. "The truth is, your attempt at sabotage did little real damage, but the way you're beating yourself up over it could have serious consequences. The girl who sits before me is incapable of helping either her team or herself."

"So what do I do?"

"Step one is to forgive. You found yourself in a tough situation, and you made a bad choice. Don't let it have a domino effect and ruin everything else you've worked on."

Christy cracked her knuckles. "And if I can forgive myself, then what?"

"This is another example of misalignment," Mr. Griffin said. "Remember what I told you earlier in the year. You have to be extremely careful when choosing your goal, for anything that's *not* on a card, tends to get pushed out by what *is*. What you are experiencing now is what happens when you have a secret goal in conflict with your written goal."

"So how do I get out of this?" Christy asked.

"You need to get yourself into a paradigm of win/win."

"English, Mr. Griffin?"

"English? In math class?"

We all groaned.

Still chuckling, he said, "You're stuck in a classic win/lose scenario, which means that you think that for you to win, the team needs to lose, and for the team to win, you need to lose."

"And you have a fix for this?"

"First, bring your secret goal out of hiding." Mr. Griffin handed Christy a blank card. "If a swimming scholarship is what you want, then you've got to have a swimming scholarship card."

"But that doesn't resolve the conflict."

"We'll deal with the conflict, but not yet. Not until after we've made the card."

"Why wait? It's still going to be there. We're just putting in all this extra work."

Mr. Griffin sighed. "I'd hope by now that if you've learned anything from the notecard system, it's that it takes you through a process that activates your mind. Your biggest problem right now is that you've become attached to a single strategy of how you can achieve your goal. When you only have one option, it's not an option at all, it's an ultimatum. When you have two options, you have a dilemma. Possibilities start to open up when we have three, four, five, or more ways to accomplish a goal.

"Every time any of you have used the Mastermind process, you've generated new strategies. So now let's engage in this process for your swimming scholarship and see if we can't get you out of your logjam."

"OK, I'll try." Christy read:

I intend to get a full-ride swimming scholarship to a top program by April 30.
To accomplish this . . .

"Wait," I broke in. "Why's it necessary to get the scholarship to a top program?"

Christy looked at me like I was nuts. "I want to compete with the best."

"I get that, but the other day, you told me that your goal was to be the first person in your family to graduate from college. What if there's a good school with a mediocre swim team that's willing to give you a full-ride? Would you turn down the free college degree because the team isn't good enough?"

Christy thought for a moment. "You're right. I've always had my heart set on being on a top team, but the college degree is a bigger priority."

"Kelvin just helped us with the next step in resolving your conflict," Mr. Griffin said, "expanding your options. The more schools you're willing to consider, the easier it becomes to get a scholarship somewhere."

"But I want to swim for a top program," Christy said.

"No one is encouraging you to settle," Mr. Griffin said. "Your Mastermind Group will still do all they can to help you get into the program of your choice. But which would you prefer: to help your team win the state championship and get a full-ride to a lesser program, or to sabotage your team to get into a top program?"

"I felt awful yesterday. I'd rather win the championship even if it meant going to a lesser college program. I see what you mean. My stomach already feels less jittery." She crossed out a few words. "OK, so now my card says:

I intend to get a full-ride swimming scholarship by April 30. To accomplish this, I will:

"Help me out, guys. How can I get a scholarship even if I can't return to the team?"

"Use your network," Jarod said. "I got so much out of that meeting with Bill that I even booked another one for this weekend. Coach Sue and Coach Dana are both far more knowledgeable and connected in the swimming world than you are. Have you gone to them for advice?"

"No," Christy said. "I really should though."

"Plus all of those other coaches who helped you out earlier in the year," Darnell said.

"That's true," Christy said. "A number of them told me they'd be willing to help out our team. Maybe they'd be willing to help me on this as well?"

"How about another video?" I said.

"You think a video showing me on my crutches will win me any scholarships?"

"I think we can come up with a better script than that," I said. "I'm sure you've had plenty of people video your past races on their phones. We can gather some of those, plus the video footage I took last time. We can interview Coach Sue and Coach Dana. You can send it around to the college coaches you want to approach."

"You're willing to make another one?" Christy asked.

"Of course."

Her expression relaxed. "OK, I'm in."

"Even if you're not rehabbed enough to swim in the championship," Darnell said, "it might be enough to get back to swimming with the team. That alone can show that you're on the road to recovery."

"You're right. I don't need to swim my best times, just show coaches I'm capable of getting there."

"And isn't it better to be part of a winning team than a losing one?" I asked.

"I suppose so. And I can help make that happen. Amanda's a natural, but she needs a ton of work on her technique. Coach Sue made it clear that she and Coach Dana aren't going to spend much time working with anyone joining the team this late in the season. If I can help her get better, I can help the team win."

"Still feeling in conflict?" Mr. Griffin asked.

Christy let out a slow breath. "Not as much. I was mostly scared of losing out on college. But everything you guys said is right. If I attack my scholarship applications with the same intensity I put into getting a new coach, I have a chance even if I'm not the best on the team. And when I think that way, I feel more selfish than ever for putting myself ahead of the team. I'm captain, and I've dedicated myself to building a winning team. I won't let my hunt for a scholarship get in the way of doing what's best for them."

Jarod's foot jittered on the floor. "What happens if we have a conflict that won't go away so easily?" he asked Mr. Griffin. "I mean, winning a championship and getting a scholarship don't contradict. But what if you want to get one job in Texas and another in Michigan. You can't take them both."

"Remember, your cards are barometers. Darnell lost passion for his card because his goal changed. Each day he felt dissatisfaction when reading his card, which indicated he needed to shift direction. In your example, you'd make a card for each job. There's no reason why you can't apply for them both. As you read them, pay attention to which card moves you.

"The cards are nothing on their own. They're only valuable for what they stir up in you. First, see if there's a way you can make both goals work so they don't contradict, as Christy just did. But even if they conflict, try reading them for a few days, and see if the cards themselves can't show you which direction is the right one."

* * *

Jarod came into class on Monday morning pale-faced. I'd only seen him look this way once previously, right before he told us he wanted to start participating in class.

Mr. Griffin picked right up on it. "Jarod, did something happen this weekend with Bill?"

"You could say that."

"*Well?*" Christy said.

"We were riding in his truck to the job, and I told him how much more money I was making now that I got myself a plow."

Jarod scrunched up his face and went back into his imitation of Bill. "Tell me something I don't know."

"Then I asked him if there was any other equipment he thought I should buy like I did with the plow. He said, 'Buy it? Why the hell would you buy it? Remember this, boy, cash is the lifeblood of your business. Run out of that, you're out of business. Lease dammit. Finance if you have to. But never buy outright a damn thing unless it's at fire-sale prices.'

"Then he looked me up and down and said, 'you do have cash, don't you?'"

"Sure, I have cash, I said. In fact, I've almost got enough saved up for my first year of college."

"'College? What the hell do you want to go to college for? I've got college wimps begging me for $12 an hour. Hell, I figured you only called 'cause you had the backbone to start a landscaping business of your own.'"

Jarod's face returned to its still, shocked expression.

"Then what happened?" Christy asked.

"Nothing."

"You spent the whole day with him, and that's all that happened?"

"Bill's not a big talker. And I suddenly had a lot on my mind. Haven't stopped thinking about it since."

"Twice so far in this class," Mr. Griffin said, "students experienced one of those moments that define a lifetime. Darnell had his after binging on Thanksgiving, and Christy hers after her accident. Such moments are not reserved for times of crisis. I do believe, Jarod, that this is yours."

"You might be right," Jarod said.

"If you put all your focus on building a landscaping business, your life will move in one direction. If you pursue a degree, it will move in another. Use your Mastermind Group. In the past, I've encouraged your classmates to offer suggestions. Not this time. This time there's no information that Jarod is lacking. He's got it all within himself, he just needs help bringing it out. I encourage you all to simply ask him questions."

Darnell got us started. "What's bothering you, Jarod?"

"Look, Bill's not the first person to give me crap about going to college. My mom does it all the time. But my mom barely makes minimum wage and is always stressed about bills. She might thumb her nose at college, but it never got to me because I always knew I wanted more than she had."

"Can't say the same for Bill, can you?" Darnell said.

Jarod shook his head. "No, you can't."

"What did you think you'd get from college?" I asked.

"I don't know. I always had some vague idea that college would put me on a path to success, but I couldn't tell you what that path would be. It's not like I'm one of those people who knows he wants to be a doctor or something. I'd probably just graduate and look for work like my brothers did. But I've got work now, and it's starting to pay well."

"You don't think you could do better if you had a degree?" Christy asked.

"Maybe. But I might not. Plus, I'd have to be paying four years of tuition, and be studying when I could be working. I'd have to earn far more after I get the degree for it to be worth it."

"What about the whole college experience?" I asked.

"Kelvin, I have no doubt that you will go to college and love it. You get excited about learning and school-related stuff. Remember what my goal for this class was?"

"To get the credit so you could graduate."

"Exactly. To me, education is something you put up with and get through. I can't wait to get out of this school, and now I'm supposed to sign myself up for another four years?"

"Jarod, can you give me three positives about going to college?" Mr. Griffin asked.

"Well, I guess I'll have a degree on my resume. That counts, right?"

"Of course. A resume can be a valuable thing when going to work for others. Is that your hope? Or do you prefer to be self-employed?"

"Definitely self-employed. I hate taking orders. That's one reason I can't stand school."

"I'll still count it as a reason; you never know when you'll need a job. Anything else?"

"I guess I might learn some cool stuff."

"What are some things you're excited to learn?" Mr. Griffin asked.

"Things to strengthen my business. Though I'm most excited to learn on the ground from people like Bill."

"Can you think of a third thing?"

"All this money I've made is burning a hole in my pocket?"

"I'll take that as a no. Let's try the other choice. Can you think of three positives about skipping school and focusing on your business instead?"

"Three? How about ten? I'll save a bundle of money. Won't have to sit in any more classes. I can put that money I've saved into some new equipment that can help me grow faster. I'll be able to afford a decent place to live, rather than living rough. I can set my own schedule, with no one else telling me what I have to do or where to go. I can start seriously building my business, rather than just doing it part-time. And I could…" Jarod stopped speaking and just nodded to himself.

"What?" Christy asked. "What was that last thing?"

"Just a vision I had for the future. Not everything should be said aloud."

"Oh come on…"

"I'll tell you eventually," Jarod said, "but I don't think I should be telling you first."

"Oh. Got it." Christy sat back, looking very pleased for some reason.

"So, Jarod," Mr. Griffin said, "what else can we do to help you make a decision?"

"I'm good, Mr. Griffin. Just talking it out was a huge help. The decision suddenly seems pretty darned obvious."

* * *

"How come you keep coming to the girls' swim team practices?" Amanda asked me. "Are you the team manager?"

"I'm helping Christy with another video."

"Oooh, you made that first video? That's what got me interested in trying out for the team."

That didn't quite add up with what I'd heard from Christy. "Didn't you contact Christy after the article in the paper?"

"Yes, because the article mentioned the team's struggle to recruit new candidates in the wake of the coach's death. But my curiosity had already been piqued from the video."

Amanda held my eyes a bit too intensely while she spoke, and her vocabulary sounded like no other sixteen-year-old I knew. Though still in her street clothes, she already had her swim cap on.

"Christy described you as a natural," I said, "but said it didn't look like you'd had much coaching."

"A natural? Hardly."

"So how'd you get so good?"

"Before moving here, we lived in a house on a lake in South Carolina. I didn't have to go to school, so I swam for hours each day. This will be the first time I've ever had a coach."

"You'll get good coaching here. Both Coach Sue and Coach Dana were top swimmers themselves."

"You recruited them with your video, right?"

"It helped."

"Would you like to feature me in this new video?" She threw her head back in a poor imitation of a supermodel pose.

I couldn't help cracking a smile. "I don't think so. This one is primarily to help Christy get a scholarship for college."

"Christy told me she'd be instructing me personally. Wouldn't you want to highlight that?"

Working with Amanda would undoubtedly make this project more interesting. "I mainly want to focus on Christy's swimming, but showing how she helps out teammates could appeal to coaches looking for a good team member. Let's do it."

Amanda waved and headed toward the locker room. Christy came up beside me. "She's strange, huh?"

"Yeah," I said, though I continued to watch her until the locker room door closed behind her.

Chapter Fourteen

Upping the Ante

Darnell slipped quietly into class and slumped into his chair without even saying hello.

"Everything all right, Darnell?" Mr. Griffin asked.

"Do I have to talk about it?"

"Of course not. But your Mastermind group is here if you want them, and they haven't let you down so far."

Darnell squeezed his eyes shut and said, "I hate being the fat kid."

"I thought you weren't motivated by weight any longer," Jarod said.

"That was before Hugh rejected me because I was too fat."

"Who's Hugh?" I asked.

"The owner of *Shake Your Smoothie* over on Main Street." Darnell gritted his teeth. "He needs someone in the afternoons, but doesn't want any fat kids."

"He said that?" Christy said.

"He said it's a health-food place, so he wants people who look healthy and fit."

"That's discrimination!" Christy said. "He can't get away with that."

"Let's get real, Christy. I'm fat. Really fat. If I were him, I wouldn't want me either."

"Why'd you want this job, Darnell?" Mr. Griffin asked.

"Hugh is an expert on healthy eating. The job sounds like a great way to learn. Plus I could be drinking healthy smoothies after school rather than watching my family gorge on pizza."

"Did you tell him that?" I asked.

"Nooo." Darnell flushed as though reliving the encounter. "I shut my trap before I said anything I'd regret and got out of there."

"Seems to me," Mr. Griffin said, "he rejected you for a good reason."

"How can you say that?" Christy said.

"Hugh merely pointed out the obvious, and Darnell stormed out of there with his tail between his legs."

"Come on, Mr. Griffin," Christy slapped her desk. "You're not being fair!"

"Fair? You think Darnell needs fair?" Mr. Griffin asked. "Would you want to get a trophy every time you showed up to a meet?"

"Of course not, but this is different. The guy didn't even give Darnell a chance to jump in the pool."

"Or maybe Darnell didn't give him a reason to believe he could swim."

* * *

The next day I found Christy and Darnell talking together in the hallway. I was used to seeing Christy surrounded by a pack of friends and had never seen her hanging out with Darnell on school grounds—outside of math of course.

I came up to them just in time to see Darnell pour green sludge from one water bottle to the next, and Christy pass him a five dollar bill. I felt like I'd walked in on a drug deal. "What's that?" I pointed to the bottle.

"Our new breakfast," Christy said. "Darnell's making it for both of us."

"It's a smoothie with kale, banana, blueberries, and spirulina," Darnell said.

"What's spirulina?"

"Algae." Darnell somehow kept a straight face. "Hugh told me about it. He says it's the most powerful superfood he knows for injuries."

"Hugh?" I asked. "From *Shake Your Smoothie*? The guy who rejected you?"

"Yep. I thought about what Mr. Griffin said. I went back in there after school and told him that if his shop was for people who were fit and healthy, then I agreed that I'd be a poor fit. But if his store was for people working their butts off to become fit, he would not find a better example than me. Then I showed him what I looked like a few months ago." Darnell pulled out his phone and flipped to some pictures from earlier in the year.

I'd forgotten just how big Darnell had been—the difference was tremendous. "Did you really show him the pictures with the numbers on your chest?"

"Absolutely. He loved it. He even asked if I'd be willing to do that again in the store. He thought it would be both a fun gimmick and a real inspiration for his customers."

"So he gave you the job?"

"I challenged him to give me a one week trial, and he agreed. But when he sees how committed I am, I have no doubt he'll make it permanent."

I pointed to the sludge. "And that stuff tastes good?"

"Well, the spirulina doesn't, but you barely notice it. Everything else is delicious. Wanna try?"

"No thanks." I turned to Christy. "This is part of your recovery, I take it?"

"Whatever my dietitian recommends, I'm having." Christy squeezed Darnell's arm.

Mr. Griffin had told me that Darnell would find himself becoming more popular because he knew what he wanted and was going at it with abandon. In truth, seeing him stand there next to Christy, he no longer looked so out of place as he would have a few months earlier. His weight was probably down 25 to 30 pounds, but it was his newfound confidence, even more than his thinned-down frame, that made him look at home.

Christy gulped some. "It's good, Kelvin. Go on, give it a try."

It was easier to say no to Darnell than to Christy. I took her water bottle and tipped a bit of the sludge back into my mouth. Nothing came out. I held the water bottle at a steeper angle, but it still wasn't moving.

"That's the blueberry," Darnell said. "It's full of pectin, which can make this pretty solid. Tilt it back farther."

So I did, until a big glob fell out onto my face. I slurped some down, then wiped the green slime from my lips. "Certainly tastes better than it looks," I said.

"Tastes better than it looks," Darnell repeated. "Perhaps that will be the name of my new restaurant."

Christy laughed and gave his arm another squeeze. "Off to English."

* * *

"Giant storm is on its way," Jarod said as he walked into class. "Could be the biggest of the winter."

"No wonder you've got a spring in your step," Mr. Griffin said.

"Yep. The winter has been feast or famine. I got lucky that the first frost came so late this year—it really extended my mowing season—but that's long gone now. There's no regular work with plowing. After weeks of famine, I'm looking forward to some feast."

"Do you feel prepared?"

"Fairly. During that last storm, I thought of a number of things I could do better, but I'm kind of out of ideas. I'd love to hear if my Mastermind group has any suggestions."

"I could start earlier," I said.

"Oh, no doubt." Jarod rustled my hair. "I intend to get you up at the crack of dawn this time—if I let you sleep that late."

"Could you charge any more?" Christy asked.

"A little. Last time, I undercharged early in the day, but there's only so high I can go before my customers turn elsewhere."

"Remember how long it took us to get gas last time?" I said.

"Yeah, we drove by three closed gas stations until we came to one that was open."

"What if you bought a couple of gas cans and kept them in the back of the pickup?"

"I like that. I could easily save a half hour of plowing time doing that. Anyone have anything else?"

No one spoke.

"Mr. Griffin, you have any ideas for me?"

"Many. But I'm all too aware that if I start sharing my ideas, all of you will bottle up and stop developing your own."

"Oh, come on. Can't you at least give me a hint?"

"A hint?" Mr. Griffin began the pacing we'd come to know as the sign of a new lesson. "Very well. There are two types of growth, incremental and exponential."

"Do you think you could give me a hint in English?"

"Think of incremental growth as growing within your existing constraints, and exponential growth as eliminating at least one constraint."

"Sorry, Mr. Griffin, but I haven't the slightest clue what you're talking about."

"Tell me, what limits the number of driveways you can plow in a storm?"

"There's only so much I can do. Last time I worked an 18 hour day, and I really can't do any more than that."

"Exactly. The number of hours you can work in a day is a constraint. By carrying extra gas you've figured out how to get more productive time out of those 18 hours, but you haven't eliminated the constraint. You're only making yourself incrementally more productive. Thus, incremental growth.

"The same applies to charging a little bit more per driveway. You haven't removed the upper limit of how much people are willing to pay, you've just inched incrementally closer to that limit."

"So what would be an example of exponential growth?"

"Replacing your snow blower with a plow. With the snow blower, you could only do so many driveways per day. That was a constraint. When you switched to the plow, you completely shattered that constraint."

"Well, sort of. I'm still constrained by how many I can do in a day."

"Of course. When you destroy one constraint, another will always come to take its place. But the upper limit of the plow is much higher than that of the snow blower."

"So you're saying that I need to destroy some of my other constraints?"

"Absolutely not. There's nothing wrong with incremental growth. Incremental changes are almost always easier to make than exponential, and they tend to come with fewer complications."

"But also a lower ceiling, right?" I asked.

"Precisely, Kelvin."

"I'm not fully following," Christy said. "Can you give an example of when you might not want exponential growth?"

"Certainly, Christy. On the first day of class, you said you wanted to be a physical therapist. Let's say you open up a solo practice. What would your constraints be?"

"Well, like Jarod, there's only so many people I can see in a week, and only so much I can get away with charging."

"Precisely. Darnell, can you think of one way that Christy could break those constraints to achieve exponential growth?"

"Well," Darnell tapped his knee with his pen, "I guess she could hire more people."

"Excellent. She could move into a bigger office and hire five associates, and suddenly she could be tending to far more clients. Kelvin, can you think of another?"

I chewed on the dry skin on my lip. "She could create an online course with exercises that people can do at home, and that way she could potentially help thousands of people worldwide."

"Very creative, Kelvin. So now let's return to Christy's question of why you might not want to aim for exponential growth. Darnell, let's say that Christy came to you for advice at a time when only 50% of her treatment hours were full, and she was charging near the low end of what physical therapists charge. Would you encourage her to hire associates?"

"No, first I'd tell her to fill up all of her available hours."

"So once her hours were full, would you then tell her to hire associates?"

"No, I'd tell her to raise her rates."

"When would you tell her to hire associates?"

"I guess," Darnell said, "when she's already charging the most people will pay, and she's still got more people than she can handle."

"Well done, Darnell. In this example, Christy had constraints on her business, but they were still fairly theoretical since she hadn't bumped up against them. Hiring and managing staff can be a huge headache and expense and probably would have sunk her business rather than helping it at a time when she wasn't ready for it.

"How about you, Kelvin, what would be the downside of your exponential growth strategy?"

"Based on what I saw with the swim team project, Christy doesn't know much about making videos or marketing them. She'd either have to learn how or hire someone who does. That could be costly and distract her away from building her existing practice."

"So how does this all relate to me?" Jarod asked.

Mr. Griffin stopped at Jarod's desk. "It sounds to me like your constraints are already holding you back."

"So how do I get beyond them?"

"I promised you a hint, not an answer."

* * *

The next day, Jarod didn't show up to school, but he called my phone within a minute of the final bell.

"Where have you been?" I asked.

"Working on exponential growth." Jarod's voice punched through my earpiece. "I bought three more plows today."

"Where'd you get the money to do that?"

"Financed them, like Bill said."

"That sounds risky."

"If this storm is half as big as they're predicting, I'll have them half paid off in a week."

"But you've only got one truck. What are you going to do, put a plow on all four sides?"

"I've only got one, but I have plenty of friends with trucks. Every single one of them was jealous when I told them what I'd made last time."

"Couldn't they just go out and get their own plows?"

"They could," Jarod said, "but more to the point, they didn't."

"So you're planning on hiring three guys with trucks?"

"Five. Three for the plows, and two more to carry snow blowers."

"I thought snow blowing wasn't worth it?"

"It's not, for one guy." Jarod must have been smiling ear-to-ear. "But if I hire a couple of kids with snow blowers to go in each truck, they could arrive after we've plowed the driveways and finish off the walks."

"Where are you going to get work for all of these people?" I asked.

"That's why I'm calling you. The storm's not supposed to hit until tomorrow afternoon. Can we do another flyer, for pay this time? I can pass it out in the morning."

"You sure you want to do that? That seems too tight a window for a flyer. I've already got your logo. In under an hour I could put up a quick website and then we could start ads across all the social media platforms."

"You can create a website in an hour? Alright, I'm in. I'm putting my drivers on commission, so I'll have them spread the word to their networks as well."

"How do you plan to coordinate six trucks? You can't just put your cell phone on the website. You need a proper dispatch or something."

"That's the other thing I wanted to talk to you about."

* * *

"Stop staring at the wall!" Christy screamed.

Amanda pounded her arm into the water. "I don't want to ram into it."

"Every time you turn to look, you slow yourself down."

"Not as slow as I'll go if my head smacks into the wall!"

Christy clenched her fists, but I fought back a laugh. As much as I wanted Amanda to improve, I sympathized with her fear of smacking into a wall that she wasn't even allowed to look at. Of course, I had problems of my own. After almost a week solid of playing dispatch for Jarod during the winter storm that wouldn't stop, the skies cleared at last, and I finally got to work on Christy's scholarship video. To get this segment right, I needed to film Christy coaching Amanda through the turn. Neither Christy berating Amanda, nor Amanda's sarcastic replies, would persuade a college coach to take a chance on Christy.

"Christy, do you think for five minutes you could pretend to offer helpful advice, and Amanda, could you pretend to listen thoughtfully, like she's actually helping you?"

Amanda said, "You think the college coaches will play along and pretend to offer her a scholarship?"

"You'd better learn this turn fast, Amanda. In another four days, I'm going to get back in this pool and kick your ass."

"Bring it, Bride."

"Bride? Bride?" Christy turned on me, holding out her crutch like a weapon. "You told her my Bride of Frankenstein comment?"

I held the video camera out between us. "Careful, Christy. If you hit the camera all our footage will be gone, and your scholarship chances with it."

162

Her eyes narrowed. "You're bluffing. I bet you uploaded last week's footage within an hour of filming."

"Maybe I did, maybe I didn't. You feeling lucky?" I asked in my best Clint Eastwood voice, which admittedly wasn't very good.

Christy grinned, for half a second. With me at least she could still joke around. But then Amanda laughed, a loud cackle of a laugh that must only exist in homeschoolers—school would have beat it out of her in a week. Like everything else Amanda did, this drew Christy's ire.

Fortunately, Coach Sue chose this moment to walk over. "OK," she said to Amanda, "show me what you've got."

Amanda swam toward the wall, flipped over and pushed off.

"Much better," Coach Sue said. "Good job, both of you."

Coach Sue walked off, and Christy hobbled after her. Once out of earshot, I turned to Amanda, "Why'd you do it so much better for Coach Sue?"

"It's cold in the pool. The steam coming out of Christy's ears warms me up."

Amanda's social conflicts didn't end with Christy. When she wasn't in the pool, she'd usually pull those glasses of hers over her swim cap and read. The other girls on the team glanced her way and spoke in hushed tones. Was she oblivious of the fact that everyone made fun of her, or did she just not care?

With enough cutting and pasting, I finally got a decent video made, splicing together one of Christy's instructions from the very beginning of practice and the flip turn that Amanda did for Coach Sue near the end.

Mr. Griffin, with his bizarre ability to sense what was going on, started on this subject the next day.

"So Christy, how's it going with Amanda?"

"She's driving me nuts."

"Why?"

"She's weird."

"How's her swimming coming along?"

"It's getting there. It seems like she's not getting anything in practice. But then the next day she'll come in way better."

"You think she's practicing during the day?" Jarod asked.

"Maybe. Guess that's a benefit of not being in school. But sometimes I think she holds herself back just to piss me off."

I didn't dare share what Amanda told me the day before, but Christy must have caught the grin on my face. "She's especially obnoxious when Kelvin's around. I think she's got a crush on him."

A crush on me? Since when was anyone ever interested in me? Fortunately,

Mr. Griffin took the conversation in a different direction. "You never put Amanda onto your cards, did you?" he asked.

"How did you know?"

Mr. Griffin sighed. "You must understand that the cards work on both the conscious and subconscious level. You begrudgingly decided to work with Amanda, but we all know it went against the grain of what you wanted deep down. Is it any wonder you're feeling friction? Use the cards to get yourself in alignment."

Christy pulled out her swimming card. "There," she said, "I just added training Amanda among the steps I'll take to win the championship. Happy?"

"Why should it matter if I'm happy?" Mr. Griffin asked. "How do you feel?"

"I can't wait to get back in that pool and pulverize her."

Mr. Griffin laughed. "Well, as we've all learned by now, sometimes the notecards take time."

* * *

"I've got a problem," Jarod said, just after the bell rang at the beginning of class.

"What's that, Jarod?" Mr. Griffin asked. "I thought things were going well?"

"They are. Too well. I'm no longer stretching myself."

"Ah, very astute, Jarod," Mr. Griffin said, raising an eyebrow. "Does anyone else see the problem here?"

Christy asked, "Is it like in lifting weights, where you need to keep pushing yourself at the edge of your abilities to grow stronger?"

"Precisely. Growth rarely happens within your comfort zone," Mr. Griffin said. "Once you grow yourself, you need to grow your goals as well, or else you'll find yourself stagnating again."

"I never thought I'd ask a teacher for this," Jarod said, "but I want more homework."

"Homework?"

"Yeah. Before, when I thought I was going to college, I figured I'd have plenty of time to figure stuff out. Now that I'm going into business for myself, there are tons of things I need to learn."

"I know little about the landscaping business. What are you hoping I can teach you?"

"I guess how to find the answers within myself. That's mainly what you've done so far. Haven't you got any more tricks up your sleeve?"

"Tricks? Very well. If you want tricks, I'll give you tricks."

Chapter Fifteen

The Lovely Miss Monica

My pen was still moving when Mr. Griffin barked out, "Write another."
I wrote the number 38 on the margin of the page, thought for just a split second, then wrote down, *build a six-pack*. I wasn't sure where this goal had come from, I'd never been one to work out, nor was I all that into muscles. Before I could change it, Mr. Griffin said, "Another one."

39. Take Megan to Fireman's Carnival. We'd loved going when we were younger but hadn't been in years. Why not go together?

We'd been at this the last half of class. It was our own fault—we shouldn't have encouraged Mr. Griffin to push us further. All we'd done is write down goal after goal after goal. At first, I came up with all the obvious ones: get into the dorm I wanted at MIT, graduate with straight A's this semester, etc. But it didn't take long to run out of things I knew I wanted.

Yet, somehow, each time Mr. Griffin called for another goal, I thought of something to write, as if the goals had been sitting somewhere in my subconscious the entire time.

"Another."

My hand was cramping up, but I wouldn't quit. *40. Interview Monica Grey.* Where had that idea come from? But as soon as I had it on paper, I knew it was something I'd wanted to do from the moment Christy told me about Monica's antidepressants and bulimia.

"Pens down," Mr. Griffin called. Pens hit desks with a clang. Darnell rubbed his palms, and I stretched my cramped fingers.

Mr. Griffin also had a list of goals in front of him, having kept pace with us throughout class. "The bell's about to ring," he said, "but it's important to never leave a goal-making session without taking steps towards implementation."

"You expect us to take steps on 40 goals?" Jarod asked.

"Weren't you the one who asked me to push you?"

Jarod opened his mouth to respond, but Mr. Griffin laughed. "Don't worry, Jarod, I'm not going to make you work on all 40. You'll find that just putting them on paper, even if you do nothing else, will have a huge impact. Your homework will be to take steps on just one of the goals you wrote down."

"So we can pick which one we work on?" Darnell asked.

"No, Darnell. You're already working on many of the goals you wrote down. The point of this exercise is to bring new goals to your awareness, to discover desires hiding beneath the surface."

"So which one do we do for homework?" Christy asked.

The bell rang. As we got to our feet, Mr. Griffin said, "I expect each of you to take concrete action on your goal by class tomorrow. You'll each work on the one you wrote down last."

Crap.

*　*　*

I picked up my phone, pulled up Christy from my list of contacts, and put the phone down. Again.

This was crazy. It wasn't that big of a deal.

I pulled out my Identity card and read out, "I am adventurous. I am inquisitive. I am bold." If I was all those things, then I ought to be able to make this damn call.

Christy picked up on the second ring. "Hi, Kelvin, what's up?"

"I need your help with my homework."

"You? Need help on homework? For which class?"

"Math. Goal number 40."

"Oh. What did you write?"

I swallowed. "Interview Monica Grey."

"Interview her?" Christy's voice grew quiet. "Why?"

I exhaled louder than I wanted to. "That day I came to your house, you caught me by surprise when you told me about your friends being on antidepressants."

"Of course, because you thought if a girl is popular, she must be happy. Right?"

"Pretty naive, I know."

"So why interview Monica?"

I hesitated. How could I explain this?

Fortunately, Christy was quicker than me. "You still haven't let it go, have you? You still feel like it's all some big mistake and cheerleaders shouldn't have any problems, don't you?"

"I guess I do."

"So why Monica?"

I'd never told anyone this, aside from Mr. Griffin. But if I was going to do this, I might as well go all the way and tell Christy the full truth. "My first Outcome Card, one that I never shared with any of you, was to take Monica out on a date."

"Oh." There was a pause on the other end of the line. "You've dropped that, right?"

"Yes. But I'm still struggling to understand everything you said about her being bulimic and on antidepressants."

"She'd kill me if she knew I told you. You really think she'll talk to you about it?"

"If I ask her? Not a chance."

"Oh." Another pause. "So that's the help you want? Look, I totally owe you, so if you want me to ask her, I'll do it. We just need to find the right excuse to get her to open up."

"Think she'll say yes?"

"If I ask her to do it as a favor to me. She owes me one."

"Why?"

"Do you have any idea how many times I held her hair while she puked?"

* * *

"My parents totally freaked out, but it wasn't that big of a deal," Monica said.

I sat in a cafe, across from Monica Grey. She wore a tight red sweater with a low-cut neckline; her curls framed her long face and rolled down her shoulders. The scent of her perfume was somewhere between intoxicating and overwhelming.

"So they hospitalized you?" I asked.

"Yeah, it was so lame, because there totally wasn't anything wrong with me. The therapists kept wanting to talk to me, like they wanted to convince me that there was something wrong with being thin. If my parents actually knew what I was getting out of the hospital, they never would've sent me."

"What did you get out of it?"

"There were a bunch of girls there for anorexia or bulimia, and we'd share tips, like how not to get caught, how to cut calories without anyone noticing. Stuff like that."

I couldn't believe how open Monica was about her bulimia. I owed that all to Christy, who in the end told Monica that I needed an anonymous source for my sociology project on eating disorders. I was concerned that Monica would see through the excuse; after all, she had plenty of friends in my sociology course, but she expressed no curiosity about it at all.

"Did they put you on any medications?"

"Yeah, they tried me on Tofranil and Prozac before finally settling on Nardil."

"Do they help?"

"Yeah, I guess."

I had a sudden inspiration but hesitated before asking. Would diverging from the subject of my fictitious report raise her suspicions? I leaned in. This close, I could see a thick layer of makeup I'd never noticed from a distance. "What do you like to read?"

Monica shrugged. "Normal stuff. People, Seventeen."

That question went OK. Would she catch on if I asked another? "And what do you do for fun?"

"Mostly hang out with friends. Movies. I love going to the mall 'cause online you can't really try stuff on or feel the fabrics. But in the store, you really can. And I want to make sure things fit just right, you know?"

I only went to the mall twice a year and only then because Mom dragged me. Still, I wanted to know what a day in the life of Monica Gray was like. "What time do you wake up in the morning?"

"Ugh, like 6 am."

"Why so early?"

"That's just how long it takes girls to get ready for school. You know, by the time I've showered, done my hair, and all that crap, I barely make it to homeroom on time."

"What about breakfast?"

"I tell my parents I'll pick up a muffin or something in the cafeteria, but I usually don't bother."

I was thinking about my next question when all of a sudden, Monica blurted out, "You know, you're a really nice guy."

Me? A nice guy?

"It's kind of funny we haven't spoken before, you know?"

Of course, we had spoken before. Last year, the couple of times we'd been lab partners in chemistry, I'd racked my brain to find things to talk to her about, and never evoked the slightest bit of interest from her. Now I'd hardly said a thing, just asked her questions, and she was finding me nice?

Just when I thought I was finally getting to understand girls...

* * *

That night I couldn't fall asleep. It was one thing to hear from Christy that her crowd was messed up, but it was a whole other thing to see the prom queen up close and realize that she was merely a glass figurine – fragile as can be and pretty empty inside. It put everything I thought I knew about people into question, and my mind just raced wondering how many other things in my life weren't what they seemed.

By 2 am I was hot in my blankets and restless. I decided to slip into the kitchen to grab my favorite late night snack. I cut up two bananas into slices and sprinkled them with cinnamon like Mom always did when I was little. Just as I was dribbling peanut butter on the bananas, Dad walked in.

"Can't sleep either?" he said.

I shook my head.

Dad pulled two more bananas from the bunch. "Could you make me one too?"

"Sure."

"You got a big exam or something?"

"Nah," I said and sliced up his bananas.

"Something upsetting you?"

I shrugged.

"Want to talk about it?" He heaped a dollop of peanut butter onto his plate.

"I'm fine, Dad."

And that's when I noticed it. As Dad turned to leave, his head sank ever so slightly, just like mine did every time Monica Gray had blown me off. Was I doing that?

It's funny. He was asking me the kinds of questions that led Monica to believe I was a nice guy. I looked up at Dad and studied him as if for the first time. Yeah, his hair was all over the place, and his glasses were super thick, but he really cared about me. And I was too busy chasing after the People-Magazine-reading crew to notice.

"Hey, Dad," I said, "Want to play chess?" He and I used to play all the time when I was a kid, but sometime during middle school I stopped.

Dad's face lit up like a kid walking into Disney World. "Yeah?"

My chest ached when I realized I'd given up chess because it wasn't "cool." Funny thing was, no one liked me any more for my lack of chess, but I lost time with one of the only people who liked me no matter what. "Yeah."

Some ten bananas and a dozen games later, I still hadn't gotten a leg up on him. But I didn't care.

The sky glowed that indigo hue it always does before sunrise.

"Lemme show you something." Dad grabbed a blanket off his easy chair.

We quietly climbed the stairs to the attic and up the ladder to the roof. We sat down and leaned against the chimney, the blanket wrapped around us to break the early morning chill, and watched the sunrise.

"When we first got this house, Mom and I would come up here to watch the sunrise all the time," Dad said.

Somehow I just couldn't picture my parents young and watching sunrises together. "Mom told me how you met at the museum..."

"Oh, yeah," Dad grinned. "She was something. I never thought I'd have a chance at a girl like her."

"How come?"

"She was so beautiful and always dressed just right. Look at me, I can't even button my shirts correctly. What chance did I have?"

"So what happened?"

"I wish I knew. If I could duplicate the formula for men attracting women out of their league, I'd make a fortune." Dad laughed. "Mostly, I followed her around like a puppy and hung on her every word."

Dad might not know his secret formula, but combining his version with Mom's, I roughly pieced it together. Dad had been present and attentive, he'd listened and cared. I guess I'd done that for Monica yesterday. Maybe that's why she thought I was a really nice guy. "And you liked what you heard?" I asked.

"Your mother's passion for art is contagious. She didn't just know the name of every painter at the museum, she knew their whole life stories, had studied their techniques, had visited many of their studios." Dad gazed far into the distance as the sun peeked over the horizon. "I wouldn't know what to do with a paintbrush if my life depended on it, but listening to her talk about art, I became a lover of the craft."

That wasn't my experience with Monica at all. The more I heard her speak, the less beautiful she became.

"No one knows this," Dad said, "but I even keep one of Mom's prints in my wallet." Dad had a secret, and he was sharing it with me? "I like to keep her with me everywhere I go."

We sat in silence, basking in the sun's pink-orange glow as it lit up the sky.

"I have to get ready for school," I said, "But, Dad?"

"Yes, Kelvin?"

"Thanks for bringing me up here. It's stunning."

Chapter Sixteen

Queen of the Losers

I walked through the town of Grissom with Amanda following along at my heels. This was not a date—I knew that much—but I was still trying to get my head around how we'd arrived here together and what it was we were supposed to do.

It had started a couple of days earlier when I told my math class about my interview with Monica Grey, and how surprised I'd been to find out how much she struggled despite looking like she had everything together.

Mr. Griffin, who was taking Jarod's request for more homework way too seriously in my opinion, immediately jumped on my case. "You must learn to see less through your eyes and feel more through your heart," he said.

"What does that mean?"

"It means that the face that people put out to the world does not always reflect what they're feeling inside. Kelvin, you led us in the work on the Identity Cards because your primary challenge this year was to truly see yourself. Now that you've made some strides in that arena, it's time that you came to see others as well. Here's your assignment."

I was to go to a town where I knew no one and to take pictures of strangers. For each picture, I needed to provide a caption saying what emotion that person was feeling. I had to come back with at least five people who were happy, five angry, etc.

Christy had her first swim meet since the accident that Saturday in Grissom, so I decided to go to the meet and do the assignment afterward. The team's spirits were sky high with Christy's return, and we won the meet easily. Christy swam with her cast on and was barely competitive, but Amanda was a terror. She won every race she entered. Christy cheered her on the entire time, and when Amanda, as anchor, came from behind to win the 4 x 100 relay, Christy was the first to envelop her in a giant hug.

I congratulated them both, and Amanda asked me why I'd come all the way out here just to watch a swim meet. When I explained about the assignment, she thought it sounded fun and asked to come along.

So here we were, but it was *definitely* not a date. It was a sunny day, so we walked into the main park in town and sat outside a coffee shop where there was plenty of foot traffic. I kept my phone at the ready.

"Happy people should be the easiest," I said. "We might as well get that out of the way first."

"You think so? That's not my experience," Amanda said.

That didn't surprise me coming from Amanda, the awkward homeschooler. Fortunately, we weren't in a town full of Amandas. There were plenty of people around, having a good time.

I picked up my phone, ready to snap a photo of a girl who looked around fifteen or sixteen, chatting with a bunch of guys.

Amanda looked over my shoulder. "You're not seriously taking a picture of her, are you?"

"Why not? Look at that smile on her face."

Amanda shook her head. "Forget the smiles. Look at that thick, black eyeliner. And see the way her hand is twisting the straps of her purse?"

"OK, so you find someone."

"What about that guy over there?"

"The one sitting by himself, reading a book?"

"He looks content."

I pulled out my phone and snapped his photo. "I'll put him down under lonely."

"Why, because he's alone? That doesn't make someone lonely."

I sighed. "I guess it's hard to tell what people are feeling."

"It's not so hard. Get your camera ready." Amanda walked toward a guy taking a picture of his kids. I thought she was going to ask him something, but she didn't stop and walked right into him.

"Watch where you're going, will you?" the man said.

"I'm so sorry." She ran back to me, a big smile drawn across her face. "See, it's not so hard to tell what people are feeling. That guy was angry."

I burst out laughing. "Of course he was angry—you walked right into him. But I don't think that was the assignment."

"The assignment was to take pictures of angry people. You did take the picture, right?"

"Yes, I did, but I can't count it. Our job was to identify emotions, not create them."

"Oh? And who do you think made him angry?"

"You did, obviously."

"Oh, it's obvious, is it? You want to bet? Loser takes the winner out to dinner tonight. Deal?"

Out to dinner? This was definitely starting to feel more like a date. Still, I was having fun. "Deal. But how are you…"

I never got to the end of my question. Amanda ran off again until *Bam*, she smashed into a light-skinned black girl laughing with her friends, and both of them went down. Amanda scrambled to her feet and said, "Oh, I'm so sorry, I didn't see you."

Remarkably, the girl kept laughing. "That's alright," she said. "Give me a hand up."

Amanda pulled her to her feet. "Are you OK?"

"I'm fine," the girl said, though she winced and rubbed her shoulder. "You?"

"I'm okay. So sorry again."

The girl waved to her as Amanda ran back toward me. "I'm in the mood for Italian," she said. "There's a great new place off route 89."

"What are you talking about? We were betting on whether you'd made the guy angry, not on whether you could beat up on some helpless girl. I figured we'd go ask him."

"Well, of course, he'd say I made him angry. It's that kind of thinking that made him angry in the first place."

"What kind of thinking?"

"The thinking that says that other people are in control of your feelings. But I just proved to you that you can't make anyone feel anything. If you could, then all of the cliquey brats on the swim team would make me feel like crap every day."

I'd wondered if Amanda knew the other girls were talking about her. "So you know what they say about you?"

"Of course. The more riled up they get, the more fun I have irking them. Yesterday, I intentionally put my shirt on backward after practice just to send them into little hissy fits."

"But I thought you said you can't make anyone feel anything?"

"I can't. The girls on the team are already feeling jealous and spiteful, I simply amplify it. Look at what just happened. If running into someone automatically made them feel angry, then that girl I just bowled over should have felt livid. The fact is, that guy was already angry, he was just bottling it in. All I had to do was let the cork out of the bottle. But I ran into that girl much harder and still couldn't make her angry."

"I'm not so sure I'm buying this."

"No? Want to go double or nothing on a movie after dinner?"

A movie? She definitely wanted to make this a date. "Sure," I said, still in shock, "but how are..."

"Selfie!" Amanda pulled out her phone and pointing it at us. She leaned in close and, just before taking the picture, planted a kiss on my cheek, which instantly grew hot. "Ooh, that's a good one. I think you can definitely submit this one under embarrassed." She held the phone out to me. "What do you think?"

Indeed, there was no mistaking my pained expression and the red hue to my cheeks. But Amanda had made me feel that way. Hadn't she?

Not in her mind. She took my hand, and said, "Ooh, I'm so excited. There's this new Japanese movie playing at the arts cinema not far from the Italian place. You keep looking for people to photograph, I'll check out show times."

* * *

"So how do you think you've changed from all of this work with Mr. Griffin?" Amanda asked.

I held Amanda's hand as we walked through the rapidly-filling parking lot. The two of us had spent more and more time together over the last few weeks until hardly a day went by when we were apart. I thought over her question.

"At the start of the year, I felt very much alone. Like it was me versus the world."

"Did you ever think back then that you'd be strolling with a serious babe on your arm?" She squeezed my hand.

I laughed. Amanda, a babe?

"You think reading your cards helped you open up to other people?"

"Yes, but only little by little. At first, instead of me versus the world, it became us versus them."

"Who was the 'us,' and who was the 'them?'"

"The 'us' were all the losers: me, Darnell, Megan. The 'them' were all of the beautiful, popular people."

"I certainly know where I would have fallen." She threw back her hair like a movie star.

"You would have been Queen of the Losers."

174

"Oh good, I've always wanted to be royalty. You think they would have given me a crown with a jewel-encrusted L."

"Of course, but the L would be written in ASCII."

"No, I'm the Queen of the Losers, not Queen of the Geeks. It should be written in Elvish."

"Perfect."

"So what happened then?" she asked.

"Christy's accident. That was the first thing. Interviewing Monica Grey sealed it."

"Sealed what?"

"The realization that everyone struggles. All this time I kept thinking, 'poor me,' meanwhile, even the people I thought had it together were also flailing—they just hid it better."

"So what?"

"What do you mean, so what?"

"I mean, how does that revelation change your life? Why should it matter to you that other people struggle too?"

Why should it matter? "It's like everything suddenly flipped around. I used to think that no one cared about my problems. Now I see they're suffering from the exact same issues. They might mask them differently, but they don't know how to handle them any more than I do. Rather than seeing myself as an oddball, I realized I actually have something to give."

Amanda weaved her fingers into mine. "There's one thing you've never told me."

"What's that?"

"You told me about the moments that define a lifetime, about Darnell going through his after Thanksgiving, Christy hers after the accident, and Jarod his when deciding not to go to college. Don't tell me you went through all this without one of your own. When was it?"

When was my moment? So many flashed through my mind. Sitting on the floor of the faculty bathroom with Mr. Griffin, baking brownies with Megan on New Year's Eve, visiting Christy after her accident, sitting in the cafe across from Monica, sitting on the roof with Dad; yet, none of those seemed right. Was it possible I didn't have a moment?

Then inspiration struck. Why couldn't I create my own moment? Why couldn't I take any moment and imbue it with all of the lessons learned over the past few months?

"This," I finally said, "this is my moment."

Amanda squeezed my hand. "What's so special about this moment?"

"Here I am walking with the Queen of the Losers, and I couldn't be happier. For the first time, I'm allowing myself to love and to be loved. It all stems from finally loving myself."

Amanda wrapped her arms around my neck and stared into my eyes. "If this moment is going to define your entire lifetime, is there anything else your Queen can do to make it more memorable?"

"Yes." We now stood at the entrance to the swim stadium at State College, where the high school championship was about to begin. Christy's lap times were still not as fast as they had been before the accident but were good enough for her to swim third on the 4 x 100 relay team. The team's hopes largely rested now on Amanda, their new anchor. "Go in there and kick some ass."

Chapter Seventeen

Epilogue

Jarod walked into class and handed me an envelope. "I printed this up with you in mind," he said.

"What is it?" I asked.

"That is a *genuine* party invitation, just for you."

I laughed easily. "Thanks, Jarod, but you were right all those months ago. I wouldn't know what to do with myself at one of your parties. I'd be out of place. I appreciate the invite though."

"Sorry, Kelvin, but you're coming to this one. I insist. You can bring your girlfriend too if you like."

"You haven't met Amanda, but trust me, she would be even more out of place," I said. "Besides, we don't share the love of parties that you and your girlfriend do. We prefer spending time together just the two of us."

"Girlfriend?" Jarod said. "I have no girlfriend."

Christy's eyes narrowed on him, then quick as a bolt she grabbed the invitation out of my hand, tore it open, and read. "You're engaged!" Christy pulled Jarod into a bear hug.

"I've got invites for everyone," Jarod said, once Christy released him. "Including you, Mr. Griffin. I couldn't have done it without this class."

"Why couldn't you?" I asked.

"I guess it's more accurate to say I wouldn't have. I was so stressed about how I would provide for myself that I couldn't handle the idea of providing for a family. Anyway, we're going to have a small party to celebrate next Saturday night, and then get married at the end of the summer."

"Wow," Christy said, "that's fast."

"Perhaps, but now that I feel more ownership over my life, I see no reason to wait."

"Congratulations, Jarod," Mr. Griffin said. "In further news, today is May 1, meaning that Christy's deadline to get a college scholarship passed yesterday. Any update for us?"

"I just got my fourth scholarship offer."

"Another small school wanting to develop its program?" Mr. Griffin asked.

"Not this time. Coach Dana took me back to State College to meet with Coach Jan, who's apparently kept a pretty close eye on us this year."

"So she made you an offer?"

"A full ride." Christy grinned ear-to-ear. "Tuition, room, board, and even a stipend for books."

"Any idea what tipped the scales in your favor?" Mr. Griffin asked.

"Well, Coach Dana's been going to bat for me like crazy with her old team. But I think the thing that sealed it was the high school championship, specifically my speech after we won. Coach Jan said that when I gave the trophy away to Coach Silver's daughter, she saw I had the heart and selflessness she looks for in her athletes."

"So why'd she wait so long to extend the offer?" Mr. Griffin asked.

"She wanted to be sure I could make a full recovery. It's a good thing I didn't give up on my training after the championship because she swam me hard yesterday. Once she was satisfied that I was on track, she extended the offer, and I took it, right on the spot."

Darnell opened the door, dragging a cooler behind him. "Sorry I'm late," he said, "but I couldn't fit this in my locker, so I had to run out to the parking lot."

"What's this, Darnell?" Mr. Griffin asked.

"Christy told me the news last night, so I brought in a little meal to celebrate. That's OK, isn't it Mr. Griffin?"

"Of course. Celebrating our victories is a vital tool for building momentum. Is that okra?"

"Yep, okra, sweet potatoes, collard greens, and black-eyed peas."

"That's some switch from Christmas," Christy said.

"Yep, and I owe it all to you."

"What did I do?" Christy asked.

"When you cooked us a healthy meal, I figured you must know something about nutrition, but later when I'd ask you questions, you never knew the answers."

"I just cooked the way my mom and my grandmother do."

"Exactly. Your ancestors long ago figured out a healthy balance of foods, and you just did what they did. That's called a food culture, and your family brought it with you to America. My ancestors came here as slaves—they had no food culture. Or so I thought."

"So what, they built one here?" Christy asked.

"Believe it or not, they brought seeds with them from Africa."

"So you're saying the way black people eat in America has a history that goes back to Africa?" Christy asked.

"No, the way we used to eat. Some still do, like my great aunt. She gave me the okra recipe. But most eat horribly, like my folks do. The more I learn, the more concerned I'm getting for my family—almost all of us are obese." Darnell may have included himself in that description, but it was becoming more and more of a stretch to call him obese. He hadn't shared his actual weight in months, but between his smoothies and working out, he could have passed for a linebacker.

"So what are you going to do about it?" Mr. Griffin asked.

"Actually, I've decided to take next year off and travel to Africa. There's a chef in Kenya I'm going to study under."

"Wow, so you're not coming with me to State?" Christy asked.

"Not immediately at least. Admissions is allowing me to defer for the year, and that keeps my options open, but I don't know yet if I'll go to college. Let's see how the year unfolds."

"Well, at least you've got a guaranteed place at State," Jarod said, "so you can coast right through the end of school."

"Is that what you're planning on doing, Jarod?" Mr. Griffin asked.

"Of course. Now that I've ruled out college, all I need are passing grades to graduate. I see no need to do more than the minimum amount of work necessary to get those."

"I'd certainly hoped that after all the work we've done together that you'll do more than just the minimum," Mr. Griffin said. "After all, you were the one who asked to be pushed harder."

"Whoa, I wasn't referring to this class. I'm still going 100% on all my cards. And it's not like I'm being lazy. All that time I'm saving by not studying is going right into The Lawn Ranger. I was just referring to final exams."

"Does that include your trigonometry final, Jarod?" Mr. Griffin asked.

"Trig final?" Darnell said. "You can't seriously expect us to take a trig final, can you Mr. Griffin?"

"Why not? This is a trig class after all. Darnell, you yourself made sure I put teaching you all trigonometry on my Outcome Card for this class."

"But we haven't learned any math this year," Darnell protested.

"And finals are less than six weeks away," Christy added. "What trig could you possibly test us on?"

"Actually, Mrs. Northrup and I agreed to give the same final exam to the entire grade."

"You mean you expect us to know everything her class has been busting to learn this entire year?" Christy said.

"No."

I sighed in relief, but it was short-lived.

"I expect you to know more. I probably shouldn't be so competitive, but the truth is, I want our class to trounce hers on the final."

"But we've done next to nothing," Christy said.

"Nothing?" Mr. Griffin said. "You think that all we've learned here has been insignificant?"

"Hardly insignificant," Jarod said, "but it hasn't been trig either."

"True, but if you've taken the lessons we've learned this year to heart, it shouldn't matter."

"Shouldn't matter?" Christy said. "The final is in trigonometry, not notecards."

Mr. Griffin grabbed a stack of blank notecards and handed them out. "The curriculum here is built on the assumption that students will learn only as much as they have to. It assumes that you're unmotivated, disinterested, and not fully engaged."

"Sounds pretty accurate," Jarod said.

"On the contrary, you've been activating your minds and learning what you're capable of. Mastering this year's math material should be easy for you."

"But how are we supposed to do that?" Christy asked. "We only have six weeks to learn a year's worth of material."

"Good question. Let's work out the answer together. I'll get you started on step one."

Mr. Griffin went to the board and wrote:

We, the students of Mr. Griffin's 5th-period trigonometry class, intend to learn all of the year's material with full comprehension and retain this knowledge for life. We will complete this task by June 10, in time for the final exam.

To accomplish this goal, we will take the following steps:

Mr. Griffin's hand froze over the board.

"Don't stop now, Mr. Griffin," Darnell said. "Tell us what the steps are."

"I don't know the steps, Darnell."

"Then what are we supposed to do?"

"Use all you've learned this year to figure them out," Mr. Griffin said. "Who can tell me a step we can take?"

I spoke first. "I suppose we can test ourselves to see what we already know. That could be a start."

"Yes," He wrote my strategy on the board. "Who else has an idea?"

"I've been watching tons of videos online about nutrition and cooking," Darnell said. "With all the online tools available, we don't have to be dependent on Mr. Griffin to teach us everything. We can do a lot of the learning at home at night, and come to Mr. Griffin when we get stuck."

"And we could form a study group after school to help each other out," Christy said.

"I can call my friend Cody," Jarod said. "He took Mrs. Northrup's trig class last year. That guy never throws anything away, so I bet he's still got his final exam lying around somewhere. The questions won't be the same, but I'm guessing she uses the same style of exam each year. Studying that will give us an idea of what we need to prepare."

Mr. Griffin still stood at the board, writing all of this down. "What else can we do?"

Ready to work on your own Dreams?

We've developed a collection of PDFs and videos that guide you step-by-step through applying the lessons of this book in your own life.

Access exclusive Bonus Materials at

TheSizeofYourDreams.com

and start making your dreams a reality.

Did you love The Size of Your Dreams?

Please help us spread the word by leaving a review on your favorite book site (GoodReads, Amazon, Barnes and Noble, etc.), and we'd love it if you'd refer a friend!

About the Authors:

DAVE MASON

CHANA MASON

Dave and Chana Mason aren't just a married couple, they're a team. They share a passion for everything from personal growth, healthy living, and world travel. They share these passions with the young people they host, teach, and interact with daily. Their home is open to the many students, tourists, and explorers who fill Jerusalem's arts and cultural center. They see every moment as an opportunity to learn something new, grow from what they're facing, or share wisdom with others. The Masons sum up their mission in three words: Learn, Grow, Teach. Their greatest wish is that you can learn key lessons in this book, incorporate them into your life, and use them to inspire others.

Acknowledgements

We'd like to thank our parents, Barbara and Stephen Mason and Lucy and Alberto Gateno for supporting our explorations, adventures, and wild stories. We'd also like to thank Beth Shapiro, Tzila Bublil, Tova Malca, Jacob Herman, Yehuda Diskint, and Aryeh Lev Mason for offering their feedback.

We are obsessed with the power of stories to teach lessons, to help us understand ourselves and the world, and to shape our lives. We came to this understanding through the many storytellers who weave themselves through our tradition, such as the Ben Ish Chai and Rebbe Nachman of Breslov. Many authors paved the way by teaching us valuable lessons through stories that not only challenged our intellects but spoke right to our hearts, including: Ken Blanchard, Eliyahu Goldratt, Spencer Johnson, Dan Millman, Mitch Albom, Brendon Burchard and Paulo Coelho.

Many of the ideas presented in the book originated with the work of Napoleon Hill, though we first encountered them through the many teachers who have expanded upon his work, including Tony Robbins, Jim Rohn, and Jack Canfield.

Lastly, we want to express gratitude to the many people who read our works and provide words of encouragement to keep moving forward.

Made in the USA
Middletown, DE
03 February 2019